100 HEALTHY RECIPES

Healing Drinks

DELICIOUS RECIPES FOR BODY AND MIND

Anne McIntyre

Bounty
Books

Healing Drinks

Publisher: Samantha Warrington
Editor: Phoebe Morgan
Production Controller: Caroline Alberti
Designer: Chris Bell/cbdesign

Published in 2016 by Bounty Books,
a division of Octopus Publishing Group Ltd
Carmelite House
50 Victoria Embankment
London, EC4Y 0DZ
www.octopusbooks.co.uk

An Hachette UK Company
www.hachette.co.uk

ISBN: 978-0-753730-24-9

Printed and bound in China

Contents

healing drinks: introduction

Liquid is vital to life, whether it is drunk in the form of plain, unadulterated water or in exotic concoctions on festive occasions, and drinks fulfil a whole range of functions in our lives. Certainly they may satisfy our immediate needs by quenching our thirst, but they can also cool and refresh us on a hot day or warm us on a cold winter's day. Drinks can be packed with nutrients that nourish and strengthen us, providing the raw materials and energy to heal us in mind and body when we are unwell. They have the ability to increase our vitality and even our longevity, as well as to console and calm us in times of stress or trauma.

For centuries drinking has formed part of both social and religious ceremonies all over the world, and it still plays a symbolic role in our lives today. On social and business occasions we often drink together almost as a ritual to ease communication. With a drink we toast the health of a friend, the happiness of a bridal couple and the birth of a new baby. We might celebrate a wedding anniversary, a birthday or Christmas, or we may simply enjoy a good chat over a drink with a group of friends.

THE IMPORTANCE OF WATER

When we consider that the body is made up of 75 per cent water, it is hardly surprising that we need to drink regularly to keep our bodies functioning well. Adults lose around 2.25–3.5 litres (4–6 pints) of water every day (more if we take a lot of physical exercise), 0.6 litres (1 pint) in perspiration, 1.2 litres (2 pints) in breathing out and 1.8 litres (3 pints) of urine. This liquid must all be replaced. In fact our bodies can survive longer without food than they can without water. The right balance of water is essential for the function of every cell in the body.

Sufficient water taken in one form or another is necessary to bulk out waste products in the bowel to prevent constipation and subsequent bowel problems. It is also needed to flush wastes and toxins out through the skin in the form of sweat and via the bladder as urine to prevent irritation to the kidneys or bladder. During a fever, diarrhoea or vomiting, it is vital to drink plenty of liquid to prevent dehydration. After a night on the town, drinking copious amounts of water or fruit juice will flush out the kidneys and reduce the likelihood of a hangover.

Many of us tend not to drink as much as we need to keep ourselves in tiptop condition. If plain water does not seem inviting enough, there are numerous more flavoursome ways to take water into the body. The recipes in this book – for fruit juices, smoothies, vegetable juices, cocktails of vegetables or fruits, soups and teas – will entice even reluctant drinkers to imbibe a little more.

TEA

Whether it is Chinese, Indian or herbal, tea is a perfectly natural drink containing no artificial additives, and has been part of our lives for thousands of years. Apart from water, many of us drink more tea than any other drink and we can make good use of this medium by finding a repertoire of health-promoting teas that appeal to our taste buds. Each herbal tea has not only its own unique flavour but also a range of medicinal benefits well known to those in the world of herbal medicine. The herbal teas in this book have been chosen for their therapeutic effects as well as their light aromatic flavours, and make a delightful change from the normal cuppa.

Because "normal" tea contains caffeine it has had a bad press during the last few years, particularly since stress plays a significant part in the development of health problems and caffeine exacerbates the effects of stress. More recently, however, tea (Chinese, Indian or Japanese) has been found to contain antioxidants in the form of flavonoids. These help to protect the body against free radicals, which contribute to chronic illness such as heart disease and cancer. One of the flavonoids, catechin, is also found in apple and grape skins. One drawback concerning tea consumption is that it contains polyphenols, which can interfere with iron absorption. For this reason, it is best to drink tea between meals rather than with your food, particularly if you are vegetarian.

COFFEE

In Europe, the Middle East, and North, Central and South America, coffee is the preferred stimulant for regular intake. Many people agree that it is hard to find a more attractive bevvy to get them up in the morning and keep them going throughout a busy day, but those who drink a lot of coffee may have a price to pay. Caffeine may over-stimulate the nervous system and exacerbate the effects of stress. It can lead to tiredness, irritability, anxiety or insomnia, and is a common cause of headaches, migraine, hormone imbalances and indigestion. Decaffeinated coffee can reduce the harmful impact on the nervous system in determined coffee drinkers. Alternatively, adding cardamom, as they do in the Middle East, helps to neutralize the effects of caffeine. Strong coffee made in a cafetière or percolator has been shown to raise blood cholesterol, increasing the risk of arterial and heart disease. However, both ordinary and decaffeinated coffee contain antioxidants which actually help to reduce the risk of heart disease. The laxative and diuretic effects of coffee can be useful, but may have you needing the bathroom when it is not convenient.

JUICES

Raw fruit and vegetable juices are said to be the richest available sources of vitamins, minerals and enzymes. Drunk in this form, these pass rapidly into the blood stream because they require very little breaking down in the digestive tract. Juices seem to radiate pure life force. People who drink fresh juices regularly say that since they have been doing so they have felt more energetic, their skin has been clearer, their hair shinier and their resilience to infection greater. Specific fruit and vegetable juices, chosen for their therapeutic properties, can be used to treat minor health disorders such as skin problems, sluggish bowels, arthritis and a whole range of other problems that are discussed in the following pages. Use freshly squeezed or extracted juices for the recipes whenever possible and drink them immediately to derive maximum benefit. All that you need to make your own juices is a good juicer (see Appendix for more details).

MILK DRINKS

Smoothies, delicious, thick, creamy blends of fruits, fruit juices and milk or yogurt, have been popular for a while on the west coast of North America and in hot countries all over the world. They are now fast catching on as fashionable drinks in Britain and Europe. Certainly, there is every reason for smoothies to be popular. As well as tasting absolutely delicious, they are filling and nutritious. In fact, they make an ideal breakfast or a snack for any busy person who does not have time to prepare a proper meal since they are quick and easy to make – all you need are the ingredients and a blender. Because smoothies are cold, however, they are not the best form of liquid intake in the winter or for anyone who suffers from poor circulation and a sluggish metabolism. (Warm milk drinks with plenty of spices are preferable in these instances.)

All the milky drinks in this book can be prepared using cow's, goat's or ewe's milk products. Alternatively if you are vegan or suffer from a lactose intolerance, you can use soya milk, rice milk, almond milk or oat milk, all of which are suitable for people who have a tendency to allergies, frequent respiratory infections, catarrh, menopausal symptoms or bowel problems. If you are watching your weight or are concerned about a tendency to raised cholesterol, high blood pressure or heart disease, choose low-fat milk and yogurt. Fat is necessary for the absorption of vitamins A and D and calcium (which are fat soluble) so it is important not to cut it out of your diet entirely. For this reason it is best to use full-fat milk for growing children and those concerned about osteoporosis including menopausal women and the elderly.

SOUPS

Soups come in all shapes and forms from a light, thin starter for a meal to a thick, textured soup, with chunky vegetables and grains or pulses, that makes a meal in itself. Eaten hot in winter, their wonderful warming properties are enhanced by plenty of onions, garlic, leeks and pungent spices. In summer cucumber, lettuce and avocado soups are refreshing eaten cool or chilled with light aromatic herbs such as mint and coriander leaves. Soups are always tastier and more nutritious when made with real vegetable or chicken stock.

INGREDIENTS

When buying the raw ingredients for your drinks, it is important to buy the best quality you can. The fresher the produce, the richer it is in valuable nutrients. Certain nutrients, for example vitamins A and C and folic acid, diminish during storage so buy small quantities of fruit and vegetables at a time and use them quickly. If you want to make drinks with ingredients that are out of season it is possible to use frozen, tinned or dried versions, though the results in some cases may be inferior in taste, nutrition and vitality. If you are using tinned fruit choose fruit that is preserved in fruit juice or water rather than a heavy syrup. When using dried fruit try to find fruit that has been sun-dried rather than sulphur-dried, even though it may not look quite so attractive; sulphur can cause allergic reactions in some people.

Buy organic fruit and vegetables whenever possible to avoid the risk of health problems related to pesticides. You will not have to remove the peel from most organic produce. It is worth noting that many vital nutrients lie just below the skin, as in the case of potatoes and apples. Always choose ripe fruit as they will give a sweeter taste and smoother texture to your juices and smoothies.

Alcohol-free drinks are a fashionable way to get you looking and feeling your best. The recipes in this book are not just boring alternatives for teetotallers or health fanatics, but have been selected to stimulate the senses and scintillate the taste buds, at the same time as improving health and vitality. Enlivened with a variety of herbs and spices, these drinks are bursting with ingredients to keep us feeling on top of the world, but they will also enhance the healing process when we are not at our best. Vitamins, minerals and trace elements, protein, essential fatty acids, complex carbohydrates and a whole range of therapeutic phytochemicals are all here, playing leading roles in delicious drinks with which we can truly toast your good health. Cheers!

DRINKS FOR LOOKING GOOD AND FEELING GOOD

introduction

Positive health is the goal of this book, not simply keeping yourself free from illness, but unmistakably looking and feeling your best. Your skin should not only be clear of spots and blemishes but have a lustre and glow that is an outward sign that all is well within. Similarly your hair should shine, your eyes should look clear and sparkling. Your body should move with energy and ease. These are the physical manifestations that can only exist if they mirror the wellbeing and vitality that we feel inside.

Such a balanced state of health and vitality depends on many factors. Our diet needs to be abundant in nutrients to provide us with all the raw materials for the maintenance of every vital function of the body. Each system needs to be provided for. Our nervous systems, for example, require sufficient vitamin B and C, calcium, magnesium and essential fatty acids to ensure that we cope with the stress in our lives and keep a balanced perspective. Our immune systems, vital for prevention of and recovery from infection and problems of immunity including cancer, need nutrients such as vitamins A, B, C and E, calcium, magnesium, iron, zinc and selenium.

Our digestions need to be robust and efficient enough to break down, absorb and assimilate these nutrients. They also need to excrete the waste products of their metabolism effectively so that we remain free from an over-accumulation of toxins that make us feel off-colour and lethargic and contribute to disease. We also need to try to lead a lifestyle that is as stress-free and conducive to health and wellbeing as it possibly can be. We need to balance the activity of each day with periods of rest and relaxation and get plenty of sleep to replenish our batteries. We also need to take adequate exercise on a regular basis to ensure good circulation of blood to and from every cell and tissue in the body. Only this way will each cell receive the oxygen and nutrition it needs to function at its best and be relieved of wastes and toxins.

The amazing health-giving properties of fresh foodstuffs can be put to excellent use by their daily inclusion in drinks that are not only quick but also easy to make. Good, healthy food may already figure to some extent in our regular meals but it is never easy to balance our daily requirements of nutrients with our intake and many of us resort to supplements because we feel or look tired and run down. The drinks that follow are abundant in a whole range of nourishing ingredients that, if drunk regularly, will soon have you looking and feeling radiant.

jamaican grapefruit & pineapple spritz

SERVES 4

Preparation time: 10 minutes

500ml (16fl oz) pink grapefruit juice or juice of 2 fresh grapefruit
250ml (8fl oz) pineapple juice
ice cubes
750ml (1¼ pints) sparkling mineral water
fresh pineapple slices and mint sprigs, to garnish

Pour 125ml (4fl oz) of grapefruit juice and 60ml (2fl oz) of pineapple juice into each glass. Add a few ice cubes and fill up with mineral water. Garnish each drink with a pineapple slice and a sprig of mint.

This light, cooling and refreshing drink makes a great accompaniment to the hot spicy food that the Jamaicans love. Both grapefruit and pineapple are ideal foods for losing weight. They cleanse the urinary system and help the body to get rid of excess toxins and fluid, and also help the digestive system to break down fats. A further benefit brought by this delicious drink is that it clears putrefaction from the bowels and helps to remedy constipation.

thai tango

SERVES I
Preparation time: 20 minutes

100g (4oz) fresh papaya, sliced
juice of I lime
2 medium pears, peeled and sliced
200ml (7fl oz) rice milk
pinch of ground ginger
ice cubes (optional)
lime slices, to garnish (optional)

Combine all the ingredients and blend. For a long refreshing drink, pour over ice. Garnish with a sprinkle of ground ginger and a slice of lime, if liked.

Almost a meal in itself, this exotic combination of tropical fruits makes a great way to start a summer's day. It is filling and yet slimming at the same time. The sweet juicy papaya is highly nutritious, packed with vitamin C and beta-carotene, and together with the pears provides a good source of fibre to ensure efficient bowels. Papaya also contains enzymes which are a great aid to digestion. The tangy lime adds bite, stimulates digestion and clears excess fluid from the body.

corfiot horta & rigani tea

SERVES 2–3
Preparation time: 10 minutes

2 tablespoons young dandelion
  leaves, washed and chopped
2 teaspoons dried or 4 teaspoons
  fresh oregano
600ml (1 pint) boiling water

Place the herbs in a teapot and pour over boiling water. Cover and leave to infuse for 10 minutes. Drink a cupful 3 times daily after meals.

Tender young dandelion leaves, known in Corfu as horta, are prized by the locals who regularly collect them from the wild to boil and eat like spinach. The water the leaves are cooked in is considered very healthy to drink and it certainly has a powerful diuretic effect. It tastes faintly bitter but when combined with the penetrating flavour of oregano (rigani) makes a light and refreshing tea, which doubles as a digestive when drunk after meals. This dynamic duo is recommended to those watching their weight for its combined effects of eliminating excess fluid and stimulating digestion.

apple & apricot slimmer

SERVES 1
Preparation time: 15 minutes

6 dried apricots
125ml (4fl oz) apple juice
100g (4oz) natural live yogurt,
  low fat
freshly grated nutmeg, to garnish

Cook the apricots in a little water until soft then drain. Blend with the apple juice and yogurt and top with a sprinkling of nutmeg.

A delectable smoothie for those watching their weight, this combination of sweet fruits and yogurt is almost a meal in itself. Apricots are high in fibre and low in calories and at the same time satisfy that urge to have something sweet. Apples aid digestion and absorption and have the ability to dampen the appetite, which is always a great bonus for weight watchers.

When dieting, eat plenty of fresh fruit and vegetables, high fibre and unrefined carbohydrates and drink plenty of liquid, with spices and herbs to flavour your food and drinks.

russian asparagus soup

THE SCIENCE BIT

Weight is connected with health in every sense. Being overweight affects our confidence and contributes to a range of health problems, including diabetes, high blood pressure and heart disease.

SERVES 4

Preparation time: 45 minutes

2 tablespoons olive oil

1 onion, peeled and sliced

2 medium potatoes, peeled and
  diced

450g (1lb) asparagus, washed and
  chopped

1 litre (1¾ pints) water

salt and freshly ground pepper

2 tablespoons natural yogurt
  (optional)

2 tablespoons chopped fresh herbs,
  to garnish

Heat the oil in a saucepan and add the onion, potato and asparagus. Cover and cook over a low heat for 10 minutes, stirring occasionally. Add the water, bring to the boil and simmer for about 20 minutes, until the vegetables are soft. Blend and pass through a sieve to remove any fibrous bits. Season with salt and pepper and reheat. Swirl the yogurt (if using) into the soup and garnish with plenty of fresh herbs.

Wild asparagus covers the Tundra steppes in Russia where this rather luxurious soup is popular. It has a cleansing effect on the whole body and is particularly good for eliminating toxins and excess fluid through its stimulating effect on the kidneys. This is augmented by the beneficial action of asparagus on the liver and intestines, aiding digestion and preventing constipation. The mild taste of the succulent asparagus is brought to life by the aromatic dill leaf which is also a marvellous aid to digestion.

florence fennel & artichoke soup

THE SCIENCE BIT

Don't deprive yourself, miss meals or go for long periods without eating. This sends stress messages to the brain and will lead to overeating or binging on the wrong kinds of foods.

SERVES 4
Preparation time: 60 minutes

2 globe artichokes
1.2 litres (2 pints) water
1 tablespoon olive oil
1 large onion, peeled and sliced
2 garlic cloves, peeled and chopped
2 medium potatoes, peeled and diced
2 bulbs fennel, sliced
1 teaspoon fennel seeds
salt and freshly ground pepper
fresh parsley and fennel fronds, to garnish

Place the artichokes in a pan with the water, bring to the boil and simmer for 20 minutes. Heat the oil in a pan and gently cook the onion, garlic and potatoes for 10 minutes. Add the fennel, fennel seeds and artichoke water and bring to the boil. Cover and simmer on a low heat for about 20 minutes, until the vegetables are cooked. Season to taste, blend and serve with a garnish of fresh parsley and fennel fronds.

This appetizing Italian soup marries the delicate flavour of artichoke and the distinctive aniseed taste of fennel. Artichoke water aids digestion of fats, through its stimulating effect on the liver, and by its diuretic action clears fluid and toxins from the system. Fennel, another wonderful digestive, combines diuretic action with laxative effects, making it a perfect friend to slimmers.

arabic cardamom coffee

THE SCIENCE BIT

Delicious warming spices, such as ginger, cloves, cinnamon and cardamom can quickly boost energy and vitality. Try ginger or cinnamon tea to ward off the winter blues.

SERVES 4
Preparation time: 25 minutes

4 split cardamom pods
4 heaped teaspoons finely
    ground coffee
2 heaped teaspoons sugar
600ml (1 pint) water
1 teaspoon ground ginger,
    to decorate

Add the cardamoms, coffee and sugar to the water in a saucepan. Bring to the boil then reduce the heat and simmer for 20 minutes. Sprinkle with ginger before serving in small coffee cups.

A delicious Middle Eastern coffee that peps you up when you need some instant energy. It makes a perfect choice for coffee drinkers since cardamoms not only provide energy but also protect against the potentially harmful effects of caffeine. The ginger adds vitality.

A good supply of energy, though a vital requisite for a sense of health and wellbeing, is not necessarily easy to come by. Plenty of fresh air and exercise are essential – a brisk walk for half an hour once a day will be enough to stimulate your circulation, help alleviate stress and encourage a restful sleep.

gladiators' gruel

THE SCIENCE BIT

Sustaining foods such as oats and barley are highly nutritious and easily digested. Eaten in soups and broths, oats and barley can help relieve stress and fatigue.

SERVES 6

Preparation time: I hour 50 minutes

1 tablespoon olive oil
1 medium onion, peeled and sliced
1.5 litres (2½ pints) vegetable or
   chicken stock
50g (2oz) pearl or pot barley
salt and freshly ground pepper
sprigs of parsley, chives and thyme
   tied together in a bunch
225g (8oz) parsnips, peeled and
   diced
225g (8oz) potatoes, peeled and
   chopped
small cabbage heart, shredded
chopped parsley or coriander leaves,
   to garnish

Heat the oil in a large saucepan and cook the onion for 5 minutes. Add the stock, barley, seasoning and herbs and bring to the boil, then reduce the heat and simmer for 45 minutes. Add the diced parsnips and potatoes and cook on a slightly higher heat for about 30 minutes until soft. Add the cabbage to the saucepan for the last 10 minutes. Remove the bunch of herbs and serve garnished with fresh parsley or coriander.

Roman gladiators ate barley to give them long-lasting reserves of energy and strength. This warming, solid broth will do the same for you. The sweet-tasting parsnips provide energy through their sugar and starch content; combined with nutritious potatoes and barley they make a hearty soup for cold winter days when we tend to feel lethargic. As an easily digested restorative, this broth is good for the elderly and convalescents. Its high fibre benefits those watching their weight, too.

chinese chicken & corn soup

THE SCIENCE BIT

A good digestive system extracts nutrients and eliminates wastes – this is why soups based on these foods contain digestive herbs and spices, such as parsley, coriander, chives and thyme.

SERVES 6

Preparation time: 25 minutes

1.5 litres (2½ pints) chicken stock
330g (11oz) fresh or tinned
   sweetcorn kernels
2.5cm (1in) piece of fresh root
   ginger, grated
300g (10oz) shredded cooked
   chicken
6–8 spring onions, sliced finely
½ teaspoon sesame oil
salt and freshly ground pepper
chopped fresh coriander, to garnish

Heat the stock for a few minutes in a medium saucepan, then add the sweetcorn, ginger and chicken. Bring to the boil, then reduce the heat and simmer for 5 minutes. Add the spring onions and sesame oil, and season to taste. Cook for a few minutes, then serve garnished with coriander.

A traditional energy-boosting tonic from the East, this tasty nutritious soup is full of ingredients that are renowned in China for their energy-giving properties. Ginger and onions stimulate the circulation, chicken increases strength and vitality and corn is a nourishing tonic to the whole system.

west indian date & banana energizer

SERVES 1
Preparation time: 10 minutes

300ml (½ pint) milk (rice, almond, oat, soya, cow's or goat's)
2 ripe bananas
8 dried dates (stones removed)
pinch of ground cinnamon and pinch of ground cloves, to garnish

Combine the milk, bananas and dates together in a blender and blend until smooth and creamy. Sprinkle with cinnamon and cloves before drinking.

A thick, smooth and deliciously sweet drink for instant and yet long-lasting energy. The warming and energizing spices contrast perfectly with the more cooling and grounding dates and bananas to bring a perfect medley of Caribbean flavours. With their high natural sugar content, bananas and dates are excellent foods for when you are burning a lot of energy. They give extra vitality and endurance and are rich in minerals such as calcium and magnesium to strengthen the nervous system.

ginger cordial

THE SCIENCE BIT

By stimulating the circulation, warming spices such as ginger, cinnamon and nutmeg enhance all the vital functions of the body and chase away feelings of lethargy.

SERVES 4
Preparation time: 20 minutes

225g (8oz) dried apricots
1 teaspoon ground ginger
½ teaspoon ground cinnamon
¼ teaspoon ground nutmeg
½ teaspoon allspice
4 cloves
600ml (1 pint) ginger ale
½ teaspoon lemon juice

Stew the apricots with the spices in enough water to cover, until soft. Blend until smooth. Add the ginger ale and reheat. Add lemon juice to taste and serve.

The alliance of ginger and apricots in this recipe is unusual but definitely rewards the adventurous. Not only is this cordial really luscious, it is also great for improving your energy and vitality. Ginger's pungent and warming properties enhance the 'fire' in the body, stimulating digestion and circulation, while the apricots, with their abundance of easily digested nutrients and natural sugars, provide the raw materials.

leek & pea vichyssoise

THE SCIENCE BIT

Your complexion reflects
your inner state of health
so it is important to get rid
of toxins that congest the
tissues and cause spots
and blemishes.

SERVES 4
Preparation time: 40 minutes

1 tablespoon olive oil

4 medium leeks, washed and
   sliced thinly

2 medium potatoes, peeled
   and diced

100g (4oz) peas

1 sprig mint

600ml (1 pint) chicken or
   vegetable stock

salt and freshly ground pepper

150ml (¼ pint) single cream or
   natural yogurt

single cream or natural yogurt and
   chopped chives, to garnish

Heat the oil in a saucepan, add the leeks and
potatoes and stir for 5–10 minutes. Add the peas,
mint, stock and seasoning. Bring to the boil, cover
and simmer on low heat for 15–20 minutes.
When cool blend with the cream or yogurt. Serve
with a swirl of cream or yogurt and a garnish of
fresh chives.

With its subtle green colour, this thick creamy
soup will add elegance to any summer meal when
eaten cold. You can also serve it hot in the winter.
Vichyssoise actually originated in America but was
developed at the Ritz Carlton in New York by
a French chef called Louis Diat, who came from
the spa town of Vichy. The combination of leeks
and peas is ideal for providing a plentiful supply
of nutrients for the skin as well as for ensuring
elimination of toxins from the body to keep the
skin clear.

chinese cherry tea

SERVES 1
Preparation time: 10 minutes

1 tablespoon sugar-free cherry jam
1 teaspoon honey
2 teaspoons fresh lemon juice
300ml (½ pint) boiling water
fresh cherry, to garnish (optional)

Place the jam, honey and lemon juice in a jug. Add boiling water, stir and leave to infuse for 5 minutes. Drink hot garnished with a fresh cherry, if liked.

To the Chinese, the delicate cherry blossom in spring is a symbol of youth, fertility and feminine beauty. Here, lemon juice boosts the vitamin C and the cleansing properties of the cherry, giving it a wonderful tang.

traditional english oatmeal & prune congee

SERVES 4

Preparation time: 45 minutes

100g (4oz) dried prunes
900ml (1½ pints) water
50g (2oz) rolled oats
2 tablespoons honey
450ml (¾ pint) unsweetened
    apple juice

Place the prunes in water and simmer in a covered pan for 30 minutes until soft. Remove the stones and add the oats, stirring until the mixture comes to the boil. Cook, stirring all the time, for 5 minutes until thick. Stir in the honey and apple juice. Reheat and serve. If you prefer a smoother drink, blend before reheating.

This thick oaty drink is a veritable tonic to the nerves, soothing away tension and banishing low spirit, which is one of the best ways to help your skin to stay young and healthy. Oat fibre speeds the passage of wastes through the gut while the prunes add their effective laxative properties to make this a nourishing yet cleansing drink to keep the skin clear of spots. The apple juice contributes further detoxifying actions by promoting liver and bowel function and through its diuretic effect.

mediterranean make-over

SERVES 4
Preparation time: 15 minutes

150ml (¼ pint) boiling water
1 handful soft tips of rosemary
  (with flowers if available)
1 tablespoon honey
ice cubes
600ml (1 pint) orange juice
600ml (1 pint) ginger ale
sprigs of fresh rosemary and fresh
  orange slices, to garnish

Pour the boiling water over the rosemary in a teapot or heatproof jug. Cover and leave to infuse for 5–10 minutes. Strain through a sieve and stir in the honey. Leave to cool. Place the ice cubes in a large jug. Pour over the rosemary syrup, orange juice and ginger ale. Garnish with sprigs of fresh rosemary and slices of orange.

A sun-filled fruit cup to brighten up your hair, this spicy tango of ingredients is guaranteed to make your tongue tingle as well as your hair sparkle. A beautiful shrub, which grows wild all around the Mediterranean coastline, rosemary stimulates blood circulation to the head, bringing extra nutrients to the hair. Its beneficial properties protect against harmful stress and rejuvenate the whole body.

watercress soup

THE SCIENCE BIT

In today's world, a stressful lifestyle and inadequate diet are the key factors that make hair lose its condition and shine.

SERVES 6
Preparation time: 45 minutes

1 tablespoon olive oil

3 medium potatoes, peeled and cubed

2 garlic cloves, crushed

2 onions, peeled and sliced

2 bunches of watercress, washed and chopped

1.5 litres (2½ pints) water

125ml (4fl oz) single cream or milk

125ml (4fl oz) white wine (optional)

2 tablespoons finely chopped fresh parsley, chervil or marjoram

salt and freshly ground pepper

single cream and sprigs of watercress, to garnish

Heat the oil in a large saucepan. Sauté the potatoes, garlic, onions and watercress for 5 minutes. Add the water, bring to the boil and simmer for about 30 minutes or until the potatoes are soft. Remove from the heat and blend. Stir in the cream or milk, wine, herbs and seasoning. Garnish with a little cream and sprigs of watercress when serving.

An ideal dish to nourish and condition your hair, this vibrant green soup not only tastes wonderful but also contains a bevy of nutrients that are vital for healthy hair. By stimulating your appetite, digestion and absorption, watercress nourishes and cleanses at the same time, producing a glow of all round health and vitality.

nettle beer

THE SCIENCE BIT

Nourishing drinks full of nettles or watercress are abundant in vitamins A and B, and minerals such as calcium, iron, iodine, zinc and silica, providing the perfect nutrition for a shining head of hair.

SERVES 4

Preparation time: 45 minutes plus 3 days to ferment and 1 week to settle

450g (1lb) nettle tips
finely peeled rind and juice of
  1 lemon
2.25 litres (4 pints) water
225g (8oz) demerara sugar
15g (½oz) cream of tartar
7.5g (¼oz) dried brewer's yeast
ice cubes
lemon slices and young mint sprigs,
  to garnish

Place the nettle tips, lemon rind and water in a large saucepan. Bring to the boil, reduce the heat and simmer for 30 minutes. Strain onto the sugar and cream of tartar in a fermentation bucket and stir well. Start the yeast following the instructions on the packet, then add it to the cooled must in the bucket with the lemon juice. Cover and leave in a warm room for 3 days. Strain the nettle beer into strong bottles (do not screw them up tightly as the beer is slightly effervescent) and leave for a week to settle before drinking. Serve the beer in glasses with ice. Garnish with lemon slices and mint.

A traditional country drink to have you looking and feeling your best, nettle beer is full of vitamins A and C, calcium, iron, silica and potassium – all of which promote healthy, shining hair – and is only mildly alcoholic. Nettles can help to stimulate hair growth, cleanse the body of toxins and generally improve health.

indian morning chai

When our minds are alert we feel alive, we feel good. To achieve this we need to eat well, take regular exercise and allow time to relax and recharge our batteries.

SERVES 2–3
Preparation time: 30 minutes

4 cardamom pods
2 sticks cinnamon
4 black peppercorns
2 teaspoons freshly grated root
  ginger
600ml (1 pint) water
1–2 tea bags, Earl Grey or Darjeeling
  (optional)
50ml (2fl oz) soya milk
honey to taste

Place the spices in a pan with the water. Cover and heat gently, without boiling, for 20 minutes. Remove from the heat. Infuse the tea bag(s) for 5 minutes and remove. Add the milk and honey and serve hot.

To kick start your brain in the morning try this stimulating medley of spices which not only exhilarates the taste buds but also invigorates the mind. The warming nature of ginger, black pepper and cinnamon enhances the circulation and sends more blood to the brain, so that you feel awake and alert. The black tea adds its own flavour and is optional. The over-stimulating effect of the caffeine is balanced by the cardamom.

almond milk

THE SCIENCE BIT

Almonds contain acetylcholine, a neurotransmitter for good brain function, which is made from vitamin B5 and choline (in nuts, citrus fruits, wheatgerm, beans and pulses).

SERVES 2
Preparation time: 5 minutes

100g (4oz) blanched almonds
600ml (1 pint) water
2 teaspoons lecithin granules.
honey to taste (optional)
pinch of ground cinnamon

Put the almonds and water in a liquidizer and blend. Add the lecithin granules and blend again. Sweeten with honey if required and serve sprinkled with cinnamon.

Sweet and smooth, enlivened by a hint of spice, almond milk is an ideal brain food. Rich in potassium phosphate, calcium and magnesium, all vital nutrients for the central nervous system, almonds improve mental stamina, enhance memory and concentration, and increase resilience to stress. The lecithin acts as an emulsifier and provides choline, which is particularly good for improving the memory. Almond milk makes an ideal substitute for cow's or goat's milk.

cold awakening

THE SCIENCE BIT

An occasional tea or coffee, if you are not a regular caffeine user, can give you a flood of mental energy. Regular use will lead to chronic fatigue, poor concentration, anxiety, and often insomnia.

SERVES 2–3

Preparation time: 10 minutes

1 tablespoon freshly ground coffee
1 teaspoon ground nutmeg
1 teaspoon ground cardamom
600ml (1 pint) boiling water
2 tablespoons vanilla ice cream
1 tablespoon honey
ice cubes
ground cardamom, to garnish

Place the coffee, nutmeg and cardamom in a pot and pour on boiling water. Leave to stand until cold. Strain into a bowl or liquidizer and blend with the ice cream and honey. Pour into glasses over ice cubes and sprinkle with ground cardamom.

When nothing other than a cup of real coffee will do to enable you to finish that job you have been putting off for weeks, try this spicy version of iced coffee. It is particularly refreshing on a hot summer's day after a good lunch when lethargy might be threatening, albeit rather pleasantly, to take over the brain. The Middle Eastern tradition of combining cardamom with coffee works a treat and tastes delicious.

Many of us rely on stimulants, particularly tea and coffee, to get us going in the mornings and keep our brains working through the day. These give us quick bursts of energy followed by a crash, encouraging us to reach for the next caffeine fix.

ginseng & cardamom brain tonic

THE SCIENCE BIT

Combat the loss of brain power caused by anxiety and stress with drinks containing nerve tonics such as oats, almonds and ginseng that increase our resilience.

SERVES 8

Preparation time: 60 minutes

25g (1oz) whole dried ginseng root
2 litres (3½ pints) water
15g (½oz) cardamon pods

Place the ginseng in a pan with the water. Bring to the boil and simmer on a low heat for 30 minutes until the liquid is reduced by half. Add the cardamom, cover and heat gently, without boiling, for a further 20 minutes. Strain. Drink a cupful each morning. Store in the refrigerator and reheat when required.

Sweet and aromatic, this flavoursome decoction cannot be recommended highly enough to those who want to improve their mental performance. In India cardamom is recognized as one of the best stimulants to the mind, enhancing clarity and concentration. Ginseng has been shown through extensive research to improve memory and overall mental capacity, and is particularly useful for protecting against the effects of aging on the function of the brain.

old english oatmeal caudle

THE SCIENCE BIT

Foods affect the chemistry of the brain, and eating the right foods at the right time of the day can really make a difference to the amount of mental energy we have.

SERVES 2–3
Preparation time: 35 minutes

1 handful fine oatmeal
2 teaspoons wheatgerm
300ml (½ pint) ginger ale
300ml (½ pint) water
6 cloves
a pinch of ground nutmeg
2.5cm (1in) piece of root ginger, peeled and sliced or grated
honey to taste
slivers of lemon peel, to garnish

Place all the ingredients except the honey and lemon peel in a pan and boil for 30 minutes, stirring frequently. If the mixture becomes too thick, add a little more water or ginger ale. Sweeten with honey to taste and serve sprinkled with lemon peel.

This stout bevvy was traditionally made with beer and served in English pubs. It was considered a good hot drink for a cold night and was particularly popular with labourers to give them strength for the long drive home after market day. Rich in vitamins and minerals, oats increase both physical and mental energy, and are in fact one of the best tonics for the nervous system. The added wheatgerm provides vital choline.

moroccan mint tea

SERVES 4
Preparation time: 8 minutes

50-75g (2–3oz) fresh mint leaves (preferably spearmint or peppermint)
1–2 tablespoons sugar (traditional but optional)
1 litre (1¾ pints) boiling water
fresh mint sprigs, to garnish (optional)

Place the mint (and sugar if used) in a teapot. Pour over the boiling water and leave to steep for 5 minutes. Strain and serve in cups or glasses, each containing a sprig of mint, if liked.

One sip of this traditional Moroccan tea instantly conjures up the labyrinthine streets and alleys of Fez and Marrakesh, donkeys and exotic spices, souks and bazaars, where the summer heat and lethargy are instantly dispelled by this sweet, aromatic and exquisitely refreshing drink. Well known by the Arabs as a brain tonic, mint stimulates blood flow to the head, clearing the mind, enhancing memory and concentration, and invoking creativity and inspiration.

The brain relies heavily on glucose. Refined sugar provides quick energy but no nutrients. Sugars from foods such as fruit and vegetables provide energy as well as valuable vitamins, minerals and fibre. The glucose is slowly absorbed from them, helping to maintain a constant flow of energy rather than peaks and troughs.

trinidadian spinach soup

SERVES 4
Preparation time: 40 minutes

1 tablespoon olive oil
1 onion, peeled and chopped
2 garlic cloves, peeled
225g (8oz) okra, washed
2 medium potatoes, peeled and
  diced
450g (1lb) spinach, washed
1 litre (1¾ pints) water or
  vegetable stock
250ml (8fl oz) coconut milk
salt and freshly ground pepper
freshly grated nutmeg, to garnish

Heat the oil in a large pan, add the onion, garlic, okra and potato. Cook gently for 5 minutes. Add the spinach, cover and cook for a further 5 minutes. Add the stock or water, bring to the boil and simmer for 15 minutes or until the vegetables are cooked. Liquidize, then add the coconut milk and seasoning. Reheat and serve garnished with grated nutmeg.

The West Indian combination of the sharp taste of spinach and the sweetness of coconut milk is really delicious. In Trinidad they usually eat a version of this soup made with crab meat and known as Callaloo on Sundays after church. Spinach, onions and garlic are all rich in substances to enhance immunity and fight off infection. The antioxidants beta-carotene and vitamin C, and the iron in spinach aid the fight against infection, while the bioflavonoids are thought to help to deactivate carcinogens and help to prevent cancer.

italian tomato & thyme soup

SERVES 4
Preparation time: 35 minutes

1 tablespoon olive oil
1 medium onion, peeled and sliced
2 garlic cloves, peeled and chopped
 finely
675g (1½lb) ripe tomatoes, skinned
 and chopped
300ml (½ pint) water
1 tablespoon tomato purée
1 tablespoon chopped fresh thyme
 or 1–2 teaspoons dried thyme
1 teaspoon brown sugar (optional)
salt and freshly ground pepper
fromage frais or natural yogurt and
 fresh thyme leaves, to garnish

Heat the olive oil in a large pan and cook the onion and garlic over a low heat for 5 minutes. Add the remaining ingredients and bring to the boil. Simmer over a low heat, covered, for 20 minutes. Remove from the heat and work through a food mill or fine strainer. Return to the pan, heat and adjust the seasoning if necessary. Garnish with fromage frais or yogurt and thyme leaves. This is delicious served hot or cold.

A tasty tangy soup that looks as vibrant as it makes you feel! The nutritious tomatoes are rich in antioxidant vitamins A, C and E as well as folic acid and iron. They act to boost vitality and keep your immune system functioning at its best, detoxifying your body and giving you energy.. The onions and garlic stimulate the circulation and impart vigour, while the addition of thyme is perfect as it makes a wonderful revitalizing tonic.

american fruit defence

THE SCIENCE BIT

Dark green vegetables, red fruits such as blackcurrants, raspberries and cherries, eggs and whole grains will provide the iron you need.

SERVES I
Preparation time: 7 minutes

100ml (3½fl oz) pink grapefruit juice
100ml (3½fl oz) cranberry juice
100ml (3½fl oz) apple juice
fresh mint or lemon balm leaves,
   to garnish (optional)

Blend the fruit juices together and garnish with mint or lemon balm leaves, if liked.

Freshly pressed fruit juices are very popular and available in juice bars all over North and South America, especially in hotter areas as they are wonderfully refreshing. Pink grapefruits are high in antioxidant vitamin C, which boosts immunity, and bioflavonoids, which are thought to help to neutralize cancer-causing substances. The bioflavonoids, phenols and tannins in apples and cranberries protect against free radical damage and particularly against viral infections such as colds and herpes.

middle eastern relish

THE SCIENCE BIT

To produce white blood cells and antibodies, we need to eat enough protein, essential fatty acids, antioxidant vitamins A, B, C and E, and minerals including copper, iron, magnesium, selenium and zinc.

SERVES I
Preparation time: 7 minutes

2 fresh ripe tomatoes, chopped
½ medium cucumber, peeled and diced
2 spring onions, chopped
I garlic clove
100ml (3½fl oz) tomato juice
pinch of chilli powder
salt to taste
ice cubes (optional)
chopped fresh dill, to garnish

Place all the ingredients except the ice and dill in a liquidizer and blend. Pour over ice in hot weather and garnish with fresh dill.

Tomatoes, cucumber and onions, some of the favourite vegetables in Middle Eastern cuisine, are blended together here with garlic and chilli to make a hot spicy vegetable drink to awaken your taste buds and stimulate your defences. Cucumber and tomatoes help to cleanse the body of toxins while the antioxidant vitamins A, C and E, iron, folic acid and bioflavonoids in tomatoes all enhance immunity, and are believed to be helpful in the fight against cancer.

greek skorthalia

THE SCIENCE BIT

When the natural defences of our bodies break down we risk developing infections like bronchitis and pneumonia, viruses such as herpes and flu, and autoimmune diseases such as arthritis.

SERVES 4
Preparation time: 25 minutes

2 medium potatoes, peeled
4 large garlic cloves, peeled
juice of I lemon
150ml (¼ pint) water
150ml (¼ pint) olive oil
6 black peppercorns
salt to taste

Cook the potatoes in water until soft. Drain. Blend all the ingredients together. Delicious stirred into soups and casseroles or as a dip with bread, crackers or raw vegetables.

One of the most superb and memorable of Greek sauces, reminiscent of lunches in the mountains of Corfu dipping bread and vegetables and watching the sun twinkling on the Aegean. Veritably the best food for the immune system, garlic contains substances that ward off a host of infections, viral, bacterial or fungal, and may block the development of cancers of almost every type, including breast and colon.

malaysian ginger & lemon tea

THE SCIENCE BIT

In the fight against infection, autoimmune disease and cancer, fruits and vegetables hold a vital key. They contain fibre, vitamins and minerals, as well as biologically active substances known as phytochemicals.

SERVES 2–3
Preparation time: 25 minutes

25g (1oz) fresh root ginger, peeled
   and sliced
600ml (1 pint) water
squeeze of lemon juice
honey to taste
fresh lemon slices, to garnish

Place the root ginger in a pan with the water. Bring to the boil, cover and simmer for 20 minutes. Add the lemon juice and sweeten with honey to taste. Drink hot with a slice of lemon.

An exotic tea to bring a hint of the tropical Far East to your lips. The volatile oils in ginger that give its wonderful pungent taste are highly antiseptic, activating immunity and dispelling bacterial and viral infections, such as colds, tonsillitis, bronchitis and enteritis. The high vitamin C content of lemons helps fight off infection and may ward off cancer. The cleansing properties of both lemons and ginger support the immune system by aiding the elimination of toxins.

chinese ginseng & cinnamon preventative

SERVES 2–3
Preparation time: 25 minutes

15g (½oz) cinnamon bark
1cm (½in) piece of ginseng root
600ml (1 pint) water

Place all the ingredients in a pan. Bring to the boil and simmer, covered, on a low heat for 20 minutes. Strain and drink a cupful twice daily.

Sweet, aromatic and spicy, this is one of the more appetizing of Chinese herbal decoctions. The essential oil in cinnamon is one of the strongest natural antiseptics known. Its antibacterial, antifungal and antiviral properties guard against a host of infections of the urinary, respiratory and digestive tracts. Ginseng is best as a preventative and not for use in acute infections.

greek
thyme tea

THE SCIENCE BIT

A deficiency of just one essential nutrient can have devastating effects on our immunity. Eat nuts, seeds and fish for the antioxidant mineral selenium.

SERVES 2–3
Preparation time: 15 minutes

4 teaspoons fresh or 2 teaspoons
  dried thyme leaves
600ml (1 pint) boiling water
honey to taste (optional)

Place the thyme in a teapot. Pour on boiling water, cover and leave to infuse for 10–15 minutes. Sweeten with honey, if liked. Drink a cupful as a preventative 2–3 times a day.

Even the distinctive aroma of wild thyme as it wafts on the warm air in the Greek mountains is enough to enhance your defences against disease. The volatile oils that give thyme its wonderful taste and smell are highly antiseptic, warding off all kinds of infections, and have antioxidant properties, which may help to protect against degenerative disease and cancer. Try sage instead of thyme, if you like, but avoid both thyme and sage if pregnant.

canton watercress & spinach soup

THE SCIENCE BIT

Fruits and vegetables rich in flavonoids and vitamin C help maintain efficient circulation and the strength of capillaries, helping to slow the deterioration of eyesight in old age.

SERVES 6

Preparation time: 45 minutes

1 tablespoon olive oil

2 medium onions, peeled and sliced

3 medium potatoes, peeled and cubed

1 bunch watercress, washed and chopped

225g (8oz) spinach, washed

1.5 litres (2½ pints) water or vegetable or chicken stock

salt and freshly ground pepper

2 tablespoons fresh parsley or coriander or 1 tablespoon fresh thyme, to garnish

125ml (4fl oz) natural yogurt, to garnish (optional)

Heat the oil in a large pan. Cook the onion and potatoes for 5 minutes. Add the watercress and spinach and cook for a further 5 minutes. Cover with water or stock, bring to the boil gently and simmer for 30 minutes or until the potatoes are soft. Remove from the heat, blend and add seasoning. Serve garnished with fresh herbs and a swirl of yogurt, if liked.

Packed with antioxidant vitamins, minerals and trace elements, this vibrant dark green soup provides vital nutrition for the health of the eyes. The cleansing properties of both watercress and spinach, through their diuretic and laxative actions, help to keep us in tip-top condition, not only feeling but also looking good. Watercress and spinach are popular among the Chinese for their cooling and moistening effects which help to clear dryness, heat and congestion that contribute to inflammatory and infectious eye problems.

carrot & apple juice

SERVES 1
Preparation time: 5 minutes

100ml (3½fl oz) carrot juice
100ml (3½fl oz) apple juice
fresh coriander leaves, to garnish

Combine the juices and serve with a garnish of coriander leaves.

The natural sweetness of both carrots and apples makes this a most palatable drink and one that is bursting with nutrients for the eyes, notably beta-carotene and vitamin C. It also makes a good aid to digestion and, by helping to keep the bowels regular, it clears toxins from the system, something that is vital to keep the eyes clear and healthy. The immune-enhancing properties of carrots and apples, together with the cooling effects of coriander, help to keep at bay allergies, infections and inflammations that contribute to eye problems such as conjunctivitis and styes.

While the condition of our eyes is closely linked to our general health and lifestyle, there is much we can do through our diet to keep our eyes healthy and help to prevent problems such as dry, inflamed eyes, swollen or puffy eyelids, blepharitis and cataracts.

moroccan carrot soup

THE SCIENCE BIT

Carrots are very high in beta-carotene which is converted to vitamin A in the body, an essential nutrient for healthy eye tissue and good vision.

SERVES 6

Preparation time: 30 minutes

2 tablespoons olive oil
1 medium onion, peeled and sliced
1 tablespoon finely chopped fresh
  root ginger
1 teaspoon curry powder
50g (2oz) rice
1kg (2¼lb) carrots, washed and
  sliced
1 litre (1¾ pints) vegetable or
  chicken stock
salt and freshly ground pepper
fresh mint leaves, to garnish

Heat the oil in a pan, add the onion and ginger and cook for a few minutes until the onion is soft. Add the curry powder and rice and stir over the heat for 1 minute. Add the carrots and stock, bring to the boil and simmer for about 20 minutes, until the rice and carrots are tender. Season to taste and blend. Garnish with mint leaves before serving.

In the souks of Marrakesh you may find this exquisite blend of sweet young carrots and fresh mint, which not only delights your taste buds but also allows your eyes to take in the night life of Morocco to the full. The carrots and mint provide plenty of beta-carotene and vitamin C to keep the eyes healthy, while the warming spices ensure good circulation to the eyes and give extra sparkle.

DRINKS FOR RECOVERING FROM ILLNESS

introduction

It may seem extraordinary and perhaps to some unbelievable, but the fact is that the everyday foodstuffs that can be found in most people's kitchens or grown in their vegetable and herb gardens provide us with potent medicines to prevent and to treat almost every ill. This is nothing new, for our ancestors depended entirely upon such things and treated them with the respect they deserve for thousands of years. It is only in the last century that modern drugs have superseded the more gentle and apparently old-fashioned medicines from our vegetable racks and fruit bowls and caused us largely to forget their amazing medicinal value.

Scientists worldwide are still pursuing their search for new cures for age-old ills, such as heart disease, circulatory problems, infections, immune problems and cancer, and the world of plants is a primary focus. In their exciting discoveries they are identifying chemically active substances within familiar foods such as cabbage, carrots, beans, apples and cherries which help us to understand our forebears' use of such foods as medicines for particular ills and to reinstate these miraculous healers to the place in our lives that they deserve. So-called folk remedies such as cabbage juice for arthritis, leeks for a sore throat, onions for the heart, garlic for infections and carrots to improve eyesight have been found to have merit in our modern world after all.

There are several ways in which edible plants can benefit our health directly. They provide our bodies with a range of vital nutrients that are the building blocks for making new cells, repairing damage and fighting off disease. Their cellulose provides fibre which, because it is not broken down in the bowel, helps to maintain a healthy gut. In addition they contain a variety of pharmacologically active constituents, including mucilage, volatile oils, antioxidants and phytosterols, which have specifically therapeutic effects.

Tomatoes, carrots, parsley and dandelion leaves, to illustrate, are rich in antioxidants beta-carotene and vitamin C which may help to delay the aging process, enhance immunity, and prevent heart and arterial disease as well as some cancers. Citrus fruits, berries, broccoli, cherries, papaya, grapes and melon are all rich in bioflavonoids which also act as antioxidants. In addition their antimicrobial properties help us to fight off a whole range of infections. They also have a synergistic relationship with vitamin C and have the ability to bind with toxic metals and carry them out of the body.

The more we broaden our knowledge of the amazing therapeutic properties of foods, the more able we will be to utilize them to our advantage. Our food and drinks can be our medicines and this is clearly to be seen in the following pages where you can find recipes that not only taste mouth-wateringly good but also address a wide range of common ailments. Let's drink to your health and your recovery.

Pure Wild Flower
Honey

caribbean cordial

THE SCIENCE BIT

Coughing is a reflex response to any substance that threatens to block the throat or bronchial tubes – food particles, irritants from the atmosphere, or irritation and phlegm from an infection.

SERVES 2

Preparation time: 55 minutes

50g (2oz) root ginger, bruised
1 lemon, thinly sliced
1.5 litres (2½ pints) water
900g (2lb) brown sugar
still or sparkling mineral water
    to dilute

Put the root ginger and lemon in water in a covered saucepan. Bring to the boil then simmer for 45 minutes. Remove from the heat, add the sugar and stir until dissolved. Strain into a bottle, seal and store. To drink, dilute approximately ⅓ cordial to ⅔ water.

This fiery combination of ginger and lemon, a popular healing drink in the West Indies, warms and stimulates the respiratory tract, clearing phlegm and relieving coughs and congestion. Rich in vitamin C, this cordial boosts immunity to infection.

thyme syrup

SERVES 2
Preparation time: 30 minutes

50g (2oz) fresh or 25g (1oz) dried
thyme leaves
600ml (1 pint) boiling water
300g (10oz) runny honey
300g (10oz) sugar

Place the thyme in a teapot. Pour on boiling water, cover and leave to infuse for 10-15 minutes. Heat the infusion with the honey and sugar in a stainless steel or enamel saucepan. Stir the mixture as it starts to thicken and skim off any scum from the surface. Leave to cool. Pour into a cork-stoppered bottle and store in the refrigerator. Take 2 teaspoons, 3 times daily for chronic problems, and every 2 hours for acute conditions in children.

This sweet fragrant syrup from Greece makes an excellent remedy for all kinds of coughs. Thyme is highly antiseptic and, with its expectorant action, chases away infection and clears congestion from the chest. A perfect syrup for children with its smooth, velvety texture and delicious taste.

cabbage & carrot juice

THE SCIENCE BIT

To maximize your resistance to the infections that cause coughs, focus on vitamin C-rich foods, such as citrus fruits, sweet peppers, blackcurrants, blackberries, apples and green vegetables.

SERVES 2
Preparation time: 10 minutes

250ml (8fl oz) cabbage juice
125ml (4fl oz) carrot juice
125ml (4fl oz) celery juice
fresh carrot slices, to garnish

Blend the vegetable juices together and serve with a garnish of carrot slices. Drink a cupful 3 times daily.

This nourishing vegetable juice makes an excellent alternative to a light meal for when your body is fighting infection and you do not want to overburden the digestive tract with heavy food. Cabbage and carrots stimulate the immune system and the production of antibodies and make good remedies for fighting off bacterial and viral infections. Their antimicrobial properties have an affinity for the respiratory system where they also have an expectorant action. The addition of celery makes this recipe more tasty and provides extra vitamins and minerals to support the immune system.

spiced lemonade

THE SCIENCE BIT

At the first sign of a sore throat, the right drinks can support our immune system and at the same time soothe away some of the rawness and discomfort in the throat.

SERVES 4
Preparation time: 15 minutes

1.2 litres (2 pints) water
100g (4oz) sugar
4 cloves
½ teaspoon ground allspice
1 cinnamon stick
juice of 4 lemons
lemon slices, to garnish

Put the water into a preserving pan with the sugar and spices. Bring slowly to the boil, cover and simmer for 10 minutes. Strain then stir in the lemon juice. Drink hot with lemon slices.

The familiar combination of honey, lemon and spices tastes exquisite and provides a time-tested remedy for soothing sore throats and banishing respiratory infections. The warming spices, with their antimicrobial essential oils and decongestant properties, are perfect for fighting colds and flu. Lemon juice, like honey, is a great antiseptic and is high in vitamin C, providing a boost to the immune system. Honey is wonderfully soothing to the throat.

So that every effort can be reserved for throwing off the infection it is best not to overburden your body with heavy food to digest and absorb. You shouldn't be without echinacea tincture at such times. Drink ¼ teaspoonful in a little bit of water every two hours.

raspberry & cider vinegar

THE SCIENCE BIT

Fruity drinks bursting with vitamin C and bioflavonoids or vegetable juices packed with vitamins and minerals can replace full meals when you are fighting infection.

SERVES 2–3

Preparation time: 15 minutes plus
2 weeks storage time

1kg (2¼lb) fresh raspberries,
washed
600ml (1 pint) cider vinegar

Place the raspberries in a large jar and cover with the cider vinegar. Leave to macerate in a cool dark place for two weeks. Strain through a nylon sieve and discard the raspberry pulp. Store the vinegar in a clean bottle. Dilute 1 teaspoon in a cup of water, or to taste, and drink 3 times a day. This mixture can also be used as a gargle.

This old English recipe with its happy alliance of sweet and sour tastes, is a traditional remedy for soothing sore throats. Raspberries are crammed with vitamins and minerals for the immune system. Their antiseptic and astringent effects ease soreness and protect the mucous membranes of the throat against infection. The acidity of the cider vinegar inhibits microorganisms and, when sipped frequently, cools heat and inflammation.

greek sage & thyme infusion

THE SCIENCE BIT

The world of herbs offers many remedies with antimicrobial properties to help fight off both viral and bacterial infections. Spices such as ginger and cinnamon are highly antiseptic and taste great.

SERVES 2–3

Preparation time: 20 minutes

15g (½oz) dried or 30g (1oz) fresh thyme
15g (½oz) dried or 30g (1oz) fresh sage
600ml (1 pint) boiling water

Place the herbs in a large teapot and pour over boiling water. Cover and leave to infuse for 10–15 minutes. Drink hot.

This aromatic tisane is quick and easy to make and ideal for relieving sore throats At the first signs of discomfort, sip a cupful every 2 hours or so. Both sage and thyme grow wild on Greek hillsides, and the essential oils that lend them their distinctive flavour have powerful antiseptic properties and an affinity for the respiratory tract. They are excellent remedies for the colds, coughs, fevers and flu that might accompany or proceed from a sore throat. Avoid thyme and sage if pregnant.

beet borscht cocktail

THE SCIENCE BIT
When seeing off winter colds and flu, start treating yourself smartly at the first sign of achy limbs, a sore throat, a runny nose or sneezing.

SERVES 1
Preparation time: 10 minutes

125ml (4fl oz) beetroot juice
125ml (4fl oz) carrot juice
90ml (3fl oz) cucumber juice
1 tablespoon lemon juice
1 tablespoon natural live yogurt
  (optional)
fresh carrot slices, to garnish

Blend all the juices together and serve garnished with a slice of carrot and topped with a dollop of yogurt, if liked. Drink a glassful twice daily while acute symptoms last.

A favourite Eastern European classic, used down the ages for vital sustenance during long, hard winters. Beetroot has a long-held reputation for stimulating immunity, reducing fevers, and enhancing the elimination of toxins by stimulating liver, bowel and kidney function. It also stimulates the lymphatic system, aiding immunity, and helps to clear irritating catarrh and respiratory congestion. Carrots promote bowel activity and cucumber aids the elimination of toxins through the kidneys.

old english elderflower & peppermint tea

THE SCIENCE BIT

The aim is to cleanse the system of toxins, which may have lowered vitality and added to infection in the first place, and to enhance the efforts of the immune system in its fight against infection.

SERVES 2–3
Preparation time: 15 minutes

1 teaspoon dried or 2 teaspoons fresh elderflowers
1 teaspoon dried or 2 teaspoons fresh peppermint leaves
600ml (1 pint) boiling water
honey to taste (optional)

Place the herbs in a teapot and pour over boiling water. Cover and leave to infuse for 10 minutes. Drink a cupful every 2 hours if symptoms are acute. Sweeten with honey if you like.

A traditional old country recipe using a refreshing, decongestant combination of ingredients. Peppermint helps to clear the airways and increases the circulation, promoting sweating, thereby reducing fevers. Its refreshing-tasting volatile oils have an antimicrobial action, enhancing the efforts of the immune system. Elderflowers similarly help to clear catarrh, reduce fevers, enhance immunity and cleanse the system of toxins.

kashmir spicy tea

SERVES 2–3
Preparation time: 20 minutes

15g (½oz) fresh root ginger, sliced
1 stick cinnamon
4 cloves
4 black peppercorns
1 teaspoon coriander seeds
600ml (1 pint) cold water
honey to taste (optional)
lemon slices (optional)

Put the spices and water in a pan and bring to the boil. Cover and simmer for 10-15 minutes, then strain. Sweeten with honey or add a slice of lemon. Drink a cupful, as hot as possible, 3 to 6 times daily while acute symptoms last.

This old Indian drink is a decoction of spices that increase circulation, help throw off fevers and aid the body's fight against infection. It is also a great decongestant for a stuffed-up nose or a congested chest. Fresh root ginger has been written about since the time of Confucius in 500BC, and the spice appears in many prescriptions in old Chinese and Indian medical texts. It's a spice that has truly stood the test of time.

peruvian pain killer

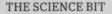

THE SCIENCE BIT

All over Asia they use ginger to prevent headaches and migraine, and in Central and South America hot chilli peppers are used, the capsaicin which gives them their pungency, acting as a marvellous pain killer.

SERVES 4–6
Preparation time: 15 minutes

2 teaspoons coriander seeds
5 cloves
1 teaspoon chilli powder
600ml (1 pint) water
honey to taste

Place the spices in a pan with the water and bring to the boil. Cover and leave to simmer for 10 minutes. Sweeten with honey and drink ½ a cupful when required.

This fiery combination of two of the most popular spices in South America has a powerful bite so is not a remedy for the fainthearted. Coriander seeds with their excellent digestive properties are good for relieving headaches due to digestive disturbances. The chilli, by stimulating the secretion of endorphins from the brain, blocks pain and at the same time induces a wonderful feeling of wellbeing.

carrot & rosemary juice

THE SCIENCE BIT

Drink plenty of fluids and eat regular meals with an abundance of oily fish, nuts and seeds, whole grains and fresh vegetables.

SERVES I
Preparation time: 5 minutes

125ml (4fl oz) carrot juice
125ml (4fl oz) celery juice
3 soft sprigs of fresh rosemary
freshly ground pepper

Blend the carrot and celery juices and rosemary together in a blender, season with pepper and drink immediately. Drink a cupful regularly as a preventative.

In this recipe the sweet, rather bland-tasting carrot juice is brought to life by the distinctive and rather penetrating flavour of rosemary. With their ability to improve digestion and liver function, and to dilate blood vessels, carrots help to detoxify the system and maintain good circulation to the head. By improving blood flow to the head, relaxing tension and stimulating the function of the liver, rosemary makes one of the best remedies for headaches and migraine that can be found.

mediterranean magic

Before you reach for conventional pain killers to relieve your headache, try herbal teas. Bay leaves, feverfew, ginkgo, rosemary, lemon balm and peppermint are the best herbs for this.

SERVES 2–3

Preparation time: 15 minutes

1 tablespoon fresh basil leaves
1 tablespoon fresh lemon balm leaves
600ml (1 pint) boiling water

Place the herbs in a teapot and pour over boiling water. Cover and leave to infuse for 10-15 minutes. Drink a cupful when required.

The delightful scent and flavour of this light aromatic tisane brings images of Mediterranean sea and sun to mind and before you know it those tense, tight muscles that bring on stress headaches have relaxed. Basil and lemon balm have wonderful calming effects and provide a perfect antidote to a variety of stress-related symptoms including headaches and migraines.

old english decongestant

SERVES 2–3

Preparation time: 15 minutes

1 teaspoon dried or 2 teaspoons fresh elderflowers
1 teaspoon dried or 2 teaspoons fresh limeflowers
1 teaspoon dried or 2 teaspoons fresh peppermint leaves
1 teaspoon dried or 2 teaspoons fresh yarrow
600ml (1 pint) boiling water
honey to taste

Place the herbs in a teapot and pour over boiling water. Cover and leave to infuse for 10-15 minutes. Sweeten with honey if you like and drink a cupful, hot, 3-6 times a day until the congestion clears.

A hot infusion of elderflowers, yarrow and peppermint is a traditional English recipe for relieving the symptoms of colds, flu, fevers, catarrh and sinus congestion. This light aromatic tisane tastes very pleasant and makes a good drink for the winter as it stimulates the circulation, clears phlegm and enhances immunity but equally well makes a delightfully refreshing drink for a hot summer's day.

Sinusitis is an irritating and often painful condition. Inflammation and infection of the sinuses develops when they become filled with mucus. Acute sinusitis causes pain and pressure across the nose, cheeks and forehead and sometimes an intense headache. It may develop from catarrhal congestion after a cold or flu, or with hay fever. Chronic sinusitis is often related to environmental pollution or an excess of body toxins, or accompanies allergic rhinitis.

middle eastern melody

THE SCIENCE BIT

Chronic catarrh due to excess toxins in your system may be relieved by cleansing drinks, such as fennel tea, carrot and celery juices or nettle and cabbage soup,

SERVES I

Preparation time: 5 minutes

125ml (4fl oz) carrot juice
125ml (4fl oz) orange juice
4 tablespoons finely chopped
   coriander leaves
ice cubes
fresh coriander sprigs, to garnish

Mix together the juices and chopped coriander. Pour into a glass half filled with ice and serve garnished with coriander sprigs.

The delightfully aromatic coriander leaves make the sweet blend of carrot and orange juice just sing on your tongue. Carrots have a wonderful ability to soothe the mucous membranes throughout the body, helping to reduce irritation. Their cleansing properties and expectorant action are ideal for decongesting the airways. Fresh coriander, like orange juice, is rich in vitamins A and C and has been used for centuries in the East for relieving catarrh and allergic rhinitis.

Cut out mucus-forming foods from your diet, especially milk products, wheat and sugar, and drink decongestant juices made with fruit such as cherries, blackcurrants, strawberries, plums, apples and mangoes, and vegetables such as carrots, beetroot, spinach and celery.

BLOCKED UP

onion wine

Take regular aerobic exercise in the fresh air and if you work in a stuffy atmosphere keep a window open when you can. It is always best to cut mucus-forming foods out of your diet until the condition clears.

SERVES 1

Preparation time: 5 minutes plus
48 hours infusing time

300g (10oz) onion, finely chopped
4 tablespoons honey
600ml (1 pint) white wine

Add the onion and honey to the wine in a large jar with a lid. Leave to infuse for 48 hours, shaking frequently. Strain. Take a tablespoonful 3-6 times daily, depending on the severity of the congestion. Stored in the refrigerator, this wine will keep for up to 3 days.

Perhaps a more attractive way to take onion is this wine with warming and decongestant effects. The pungency of the onion blends well with the slight tang of white wine. Honey not only augments the effectiveness of this drink in clearing the airways but also provides that 'spoonful of sugar to help the medicine go down'.

Pungent foods and herbs such as garlic, onion, leeks, ginger, thyme, cinnamon and mint stimulate the respiratory system and help to move and liquify catarrh. They are also expectorants, helping to clear mucus from your chest.

panamanian indian cure

THE SCIENCE BIT

Blackcurrants, apples, blueberries, cherries, grapefruits, lemons, mangoes and pineapples all have decongestant properties and boost the body's fight against infection.

SERVES 1
Preparation time: 5 minutes

45ml (1½fl oz) pink grapefruit juice
90ml (3fl oz) guava juice
90ml (3fl oz) mango juice
fresh lemon balm leaves, to garnish
(optional)

Combine the fruit juices. If the weather is hot pour into glasses over ice and garnish with lemon balm leaves, if liked.

Apparently the Choco Indians of Panama eat ripe guavas to clear catarrhal congestion and certainly it is hard to envisage a more pleasant way of relieving sinusitis. These sweet succulent fruits make a delightfully exotic juice when combined with mango and grapefruit, which also clear mucus from the body and provide a wealth of nutrients to support the immune system in its fight against infection.

cabbage & coriander syrup

THE SCIENCE BIT

Vegetables, herbs and warming spices can be made into soups, juices and herbal teas to clear catarrh and infection in the sinuses. Drinks are best taken hot as the heat itself also helps to move phlegm.

SERVES 2

Preparation time: 15 minutes and leave overnight

2 teaspoons coriander seeds
½ cabbage, chopped finely
enough runny honey to cover cabbage

Crush the coriander seeds using a pestle and mortar. Place the crushed seeds in a large bowl with the cabbage and cover with honey. Leave overnight and then strain the syrup through a sieve. Take 1–2 teaspoons 3 times daily until your sinuses improve.

This may not sound like the most enticing of combinations but it is certainly a good remedy for clearing the sinuses. Cabbage is a wonderful detoxifier, hastening the elimination of toxins from the body. It also stimulates the immune system and the production of antibodies and has a disinfectant action with a particular affinity with the respiratory tract. Coriander seeds not only make the taste more interesting but have their own decongestant and antiseptic properties.

nero's nectar

SERVES 1

Preparation time: 10 minutes and leave overnight

2 medium onions, peeled and chopped
2 tablespoons honey

Place the onions in a bowl, drizzle with the honey and leave, covered, at room temperature overnight to produce a juice. Take a teaspoonful every 2 hours while symptoms last.

The Roman emperor, Nero, was extremely fond of onions and leeks to treat his colds and sore throats. The unusual combination of onion and honey may not titillate everybody's taste buds but the courageous will be rewarded. Raw onions are powerfully antiseptic and their pungency stimulates the respiratory system, breaking up mucous congestion in the nose and chest. Honey with its antiseptic and expectorant properties is an ideal therapeutic partner.

english blackberry cordial

THE SCIENCE BIT

Don't give a child with a fever solid food, just plenty to drink. This encourages sweating and elimination of toxins via the pores as well as through the kidneys and bladder.

SERVES 1
Preparation time: 15 minutes

900g (2lb) ripe blackberries or
  enough to produce 600ml
  (1 pint) juice
6 tablespoons runny honey
10 cloves
5 slices fresh root ginger
1 teaspoon ground cinnamon
orange slices, to garnish (optional)

Press the ripe, raw blackberries through a sieve to obtain the juice. Place in a pan and add the honey and spices. Bring to the boil over a low heat, stirring until the honey has dissolved. Simmer for 5 minutes. Leave to cool. To drink add hot water, dilute to taste and serve with slices of orange, if liked. Drink a cupful every 2 hours.

This sweet spicy cordial is delicious enough to be loved by children and provides a great remedy for aiding the body's fight against infection and throwing off a fever at the same time. Blackberries are packed with vitamin C and bioflavonoids, they have a decongestant action and clear toxins from the body through their laxative and diuretic effects. The spices increase sweating by stimulating the circulation and have powerful antimicrobial properties.

french limeflower & lemon balm tea

THE SCIENCE BIT

There are certain herbs which actually encourage sweating, including basil, limeflower, lemon balm, elderflower, peppermint, yarrow, chamomile, ginger and cinnamon.

SERVES 2–3
Preparation time: 15 minutes

2 teaspoons fresh or 1 teaspoon
   dried limeflowers
2 teaspoons fresh lemon balm
600ml (1 pint) water

Place the herbs in a teapot and pour over boiling water. Cover and leave to infuse for 10 minutes. Sweeten with honey. Drink a cupful of warm tea every two hours.

This light fragrant tea with a hint of lemon, loved by the French, is an excellent cooling remedy for reducing children's fevers. When taken hot both lemon balm and limeflowers have a diaphoretic action, increasing blood supply to the skin and producing sweating. The tea also has a decongestant effect and will speed sore throats, colds, coughs and flu on their way.

blackcurrant & apple rob

SERVES 2

Preparation time: 15 minutes

2 apples, cored and chopped
50g (2oz) blackcurrants
450ml (16fl oz) water
2 teaspoons lemon juice
honey to taste

Place the apple and blackcurrants in a pan with the water and bring to the boil. Simmer for 10 minutes then strain. Stir in lemon juice and honey before serving hot.

A lovely refreshing drink with a tangy fruit flavour which your children can enjoy throughout the day when they have a fever. All three fruits in this recipe have antiseptic properties and are rich in vitamin C and bioflavonoids which enhance the body's fight against infection. At the same time they have a decongestant action, helping to relieve the catarrhal congestion accompanying the respiratory infections which often give rise to children's fevers.

roman relief

Alcohol acts as a diuretic, increasing the flow of urine, and heats the body, causing perspiration. Dehydration resulting from excessive urination and sweating is the major cause of a hangover.

SERVES 2

Preparation time: 5 minutes

250ml (8fl oz) fresh cabbage juice
250ml (8fl oz) fresh celery juice
2 teaspoons fresh coriander leaves
ice cubes (optional)
trimmed celery sticks, to garnish

Blend the vegetable juices together, stir in the coriander and pour over ice cubes, if liked. Serve garnished with trimmed celery sticks.

While the taste of cabbage juice may not appeal to everyone, especially when feeling a little fragile the morning after the night before, it is one of the best remedies for a hangover. The distinctive tastes of celery and coriander do a good job at disguising the flavour and help to lessen the intoxicating effects of alcohol. Cabbage was popular with the Romans for preventing drunkenness and as a remedy for headaches and hangovers. We know now that it contains glutamine, a substance which protects the liver against the effects of alcohol.

sri lankan soother

SERVES 2–3
Preparation time: 5 minutes

600ml (1 pint) grapefruit juice
2 teaspoons lime juice
1 teaspoon ground cumin

Blend the ingredients together and drink preferably both before and after drinking alcohol.

This sharp, rather exhilarating drink has long been recommended by Ayurvedic doctors for relieving the symptoms of overindulgence. The lime and grapefruit provide plenty of vitamin C and fructose and have a cleansing effect, restoring an overworked liver and aiding its metabolism of toxins. The sweet and spicy cumin aids digestion, supports the liver and enhances our ability to deal with toxins including alcohol.

elizabethan rosemary & lemon syrup

SERVES I

Preparation time: 25 minutes

600ml (1 pint) rosemary sprigs, gently pressed down in a measuring jug
600ml (1 pint) boiling water
juice of 1 lemon
450g (1lb) sugar

Place the rosemary in a pot or jug and pour over boiling water. Cover and leave to infuse for 10 minutes. Strain into a pan and add the lemon juice and sugar. Heat slowly, stirring, until the sugar has dissolved. Boil briskly for 5–8 minutes or until the syrup starts to thicken. Remove from the heat and when cool pour into jars or bottles. Seal with airtight lids when cold. Take 1–2 tablespoons as required until your hangover subsides.

A glass or two of this wonderfully aromatic cordial will soon have you back on your feet. Rosemary used to be sold by 17th-century English apothecaries as a cure for a hangover. This is not hard to understand for the bitters in rosemary stimulate the liver and help cleanse the system of toxins. The lemon juice also acts as a tonic to the liver, especially when drunk on an empty stomach, and helps replace vitamin C.

scandinavian soother

THE SCIENCE BIT

Don't eat a large meal near bedtime and try to go to bed at the same time each night so that you develop a good sleep pattern. Have a comforting hot drink before bed.

SERVES 4

Preparation time: 40 minutes plus
  3 hours refrigeration time

1 tablespoon olive oil
2 medium onions, peeled and sliced
2 potatoes, peeled and diced
1 garlic clove, crushed
1 large lettuce, chopped
900ml (1½ pints) vegetable or
  chicken stock
salt and freshly ground pepper
3 tablespoons thick natural yogurt
2 tablespoons fresh dill, chopped

Heat the oil in a large pan and gently fry the onions, potatoes and garlic for 5 minutes. Add the lettuce to the pan with the stock and seasoning. Bring to the boil, cover and simmer over a low heat for 20 minutes. Allow to cool a little before blending. Add the yogurt and half of the dill then refrigerate for about 3 hours. Garnish with the remaining dill when serving.

No matter where you travel in Scandinavia you will find that exquisitely aromatic herb dill enlivening vegetable dishes, sauces, soups and salads. It is the very substances that impart dill's lovely flavour that give its wonderful relaxant effect on the smooth muscle throughout the body and on the central nervous system. It is perfect in this lettuce soup which has been a famous remedy for nervous tension and insomnia for centuries.

INSOMNIA

english lettuce tea

SERVES 1
Preparation time: 20 minutes

3–4 large lettuce leaves
300ml (½ pint) water
2 sprigs fresh mint

Simmer the lettuce leaves in the water in a covered pan for 15 minutes. Remove from the heat and add the mint. Leave for a further 5 minutes. Strain and drink before retiring.

The white latex that exudes from the stem of a lettuce when you pick it is known as 'lettuce opium' because it resembles in appearance and action that extracted from the opium poppy. The whole vegetable has a sedative effect, helping to calm restlessness and anxiety and induce sleep. Lettuce tea is, in fact, a well-known old English recipe for insomnia. Mint helps to counteract the slight bitterness of the lettuce and make a really quite palatable bedtime drink.

If you have had an early evening meal and feel peckish before bedtime, have a light snack so that you do not wake up in the night because you are hungry. Remember to take regular exercise as this is a great antidote to stress, which can be a cause of sleeplessness.

greek chamomile & limeflower tea

SERVES 2–3
Preparation time: 15 minutes

2 teaspoons limeflowers
2 teaspoons chamomile flowers,
  plus extra to garnish
600ml (1 pint) boiling water
honey to taste

Place the herbs in a teapot and pour over boiling water. Cover and leave to infuse for 10 minutes. Sweeten with honey and garnish with a few chamomile flowers, if liked.

The honey-sweet aroma from the flower-laden lime trees scenting the night air in old Corfu is enough to relax tense muscles and induce a good night's sleep. Put the flowers in a tisane with the equally relaxing chamomile flowers, which grow wild all over the island in summer, and you have a wonderful remedy for insomnia. Drink a cupful before retiring.

A good night's sleep for at least six to eight hours is vital for our general health and to enable us to perform at our best during our waking hours. Insomnia is largely caused by stress and tension, often related to a major upheaval in life, a bereavement, financial worries or depression.

egyptian joint juice

SERVES 1
Preparation time: 5 minutes

125ml (4fl oz) celery juice
250ml (8fl oz) carrot juice
3 sprigs parsley
salt and freshly ground pepper

Blend all the ingredients together in a liquidizer.

Famous since the days of the Pharaohs for soothing aches and pains, this juice combines the contrasting tastes of aromatic celery and sweet carrot. This savoury duo provides a wonderful drink for all inflammatory joint conditions. Both celery and carrots are rich in nutrients for repairing joints and contain the antioxidant vitamins A and C which help prevent degenerative disease. They also aid digestion and cleanse the system of toxins and uric acid.

cabbage cooler

THE SCIENCE BIT

Nutrient-rich broths with plenty of cabbage, celery and carrots provide vital sustenance for bone and cartilage, and aid the body's continual repair of joint wear and tear.

SERVES 4
Preparation time: 50 minutes

1 tablespoon olive oil
2 medium onions, peeled and sliced
3 medium carrots, washed and diced
2 sticks of celery, washed and sliced
1 medium leek, washed and sliced thinly
1.2 litres (2 pints) vegetable or chicken stock
salt and freshly ground pepper
1 medium cabbage, shredded
300ml (½ pint) cream or natural yogurt
fresh parsley, to garnish

Heat the oil in a saucepan, add the vegetables, except the cabbage, and stir over a low heat for 5-10 minutes. Add the stock and seasoning, cover, and bring to the boil then reduce the heat and simmer for 30 minutes. Cook the cabbage in a little water for 5 minutes until slightly softened. Add to the soup with half the cream (or yogurt) and heat gently. Serve topped with the remainder of the cream (or yogurt) and garnished with parsley.

A hot scrumptious soup that cools the heat generated in arthritic joints. Thick, creamy and full of delicious crunchy vegetables, this soup will give you a wealth of nutrients to help repair wear and tear in the joints. In particular, cabbage cleanses toxins and clears uric acid from the system and makes a good anti-inflammatory.

ARTHRITIS

dr jarvis'
arthritis cure

THE SCIENCE BIT

Certain foods can contribute to joint inflammation – particular culprits are tomatoes and other members of the potato family, citrus and other sour fruits, sugar, red meats, pork products and alcohol.

SERVES I

Preparation time: 2 minutes

I dessertspoon cider vinegar
I teaspoon honey
250ml (8fl oz) hot water

Add the vinegar and honey to a cup of hot water and drink in the evening before going to bed.

A traditional recipe from Vermont, USA, this sweet and sour combination should be drunk regularly to enhance health. By correcting the pH balance in your body and cleansing the system of toxins, cider vinegar helps to relieve aches and pains. It also improves the metabolism of calcium in the body. The relaxing effects of honey add further pain-relieving properties.

ANAEMIA

orange & prune blood-builder

THE SCIENCE BIT

Apricots and prunes are rich in iron, while tomatoes, watercress and spinach contain a wealth of iron and folic acid. Drinking tea, coffee and alcohol can all impair absorption of these nutrients.

SERVES 1

Preparation time: 10 minutes

6 prunes (stones removed)
100ml (3½fl oz) fresh orange juice
1 tablespoon natural live yogurt
pinch of ground cinnamon
natural live yogurt, to serve
  (optional)

Blend the prunes, orange juice and yogurt together in a liquidizer. Serve sprinkled with cinnamon and with a dollop of yogurt, if liked.

The sweet velvet-textured prune blends well with the sharpness of the orange juice, to produce a delicious sweet and sour remedy for anaemia. The rich vitamin C content of the orange perfectly enhances the absorption of iron from the prunes. By restoring the natural balance of bacteria in the stomach and bowel, and enhancing absorption, both the yogurt and cinnamon help to ensure your digestion makes the best of this iron-rich tonic.

watercress, spinach & tomato pick-me-up

THE SCIENCE BIT

It's important to establish the cause of your anaemia to remedy the problem effectively. If your diet is low in iron or folic acid, drinks made with herbs and green leafy vegetables will boost your intake.

SERVES 3–4
Preparation time: 10 minutes

500g (1lb) ripe tomatoes, skinned
4 large spinach leaves, washed
½ bunch watercress, washed
1 teaspoon soy sauce
2 teaspoons lemon juice
1 tablespoon Worcestershire sauce
pinch of cayenne pepper
sea salt to taste
5 ice cubes
chopped thyme, to garnish
  (optional)

Blend all the ingredients together in a liquidizer. Strain and serve garnished with thyme, if liked.

The rich dark-green colour of this amazing tonic could almost have you feeling better by just looking at it, knowing that it is full to bursting with nutrients to restore your energy and strength. The high vitamin C content of the watercress, spinach, tomatoes and lemon juice will help ensure absorption of their iron and folic acid content, aided by the vitamin E also found in watercress. The pungency of the Worcestershire sauce and cayenne pepper adds a delightful bite to the recipe, meanwhile boosting digestion and absorption.

chinese apricot & grapefruit tonic

THE SCIENCE BIT

If you are feeling tired, down in the dumps, perhaps irritable, or if you are suffering from headaches, dizziness or breathlessness, you may be anaemic.

SERVES I
Preparation time: 25 minutes

4–6 dried apricots
2 teaspoons honey
300ml (½ pint) grapefruit juice
ground nutmeg, to serve

Cook the apricots in enough water to cover, until soft. Drain. Stir in the honey while the apricots are hot. Add the grapefruit juice and liquidize. Sprinkle with nutmeg before drinking.

To the Chinese both apricots and grapefruit have a sweet-and-sour flavour. Apricots have a reputation as an energy tonic, while grapefruit benefits the stomach and restores the harmony of stomach chi. Honey is eaten by the Chinese to improve digestion and for anaemia. The iron in the apricots and the folic acid and vitamin C in the grapefruit combine to make this delicious thirst-quenching drink an ideal remedy for those who are run down or anaemic.

french garlic soup

THE SCIENCE BIT

If you treat yourself on a regular basis to drinks containing specific foods such as garlic, onions, beans and celery with an ability to lower blood pressure, you will certainly be doing your arteries some favours.

SERVES 4

Preparation time: 35 minutes

1 tablespoon olive oil

2 onions, peeled and sliced

900ml (1½ pints) vegetable or
   chicken stock

1 head of garlic, cloves peeled

1 tablespoon chopped coriander
   leaves

1 tablespoon chopped parsley
   leaves

salt and freshly ground pepper

1 tablespoon lemon juice

toasted slices of French bread,
   to serve (optional)

Heat the oil in a saucepan and cook the onions for 5 minutes. Add the stock, garlic, two thirds of the herbs, and seasoning. Bring to the boil and simmer, covered, for 20 minutes. Remove from the heat, blend and stir in the lemon juice. Return to the heat and adjust the seasoning. Garnish with the remaining herbs and serve with toasted slices of French bread, if liked.

If like the French you love your garlic, then this pungent herby soup is an exquisitely pleasurable way to take a medicine for high blood pressure. For centuries all over the world, garlic has been believed to lower blood pressure. It reduces harmful cholesterol, opens the arteries and improves blood flow through them, helping to reduce heart attacks and strokes. The addition of coriander, parsley and lemon juice tastes like a stroke of genius and may even reduce the antisocial effects of garlic by sweetening your breath.

spanish gazpacho

THE SCIENCE BIT

An abundance of fresh fruit and vegetables, pulses, nuts, seeds, some fatty fish and tofu will boost your intake of precious minerals for regulating blood pressure.

SERVES 4

Preparation time: 30 minutes plus
   6 hours chilling time

½ medium cucumber
1 large onion
3 garlic cloves
3 tomatoes, chopped
2 tablespoons olive oil
2 tablespoons white wine vinegar
1 tablespoon lemon juice
1 dessertspoon tomato purée
1 teaspoon pesto sauce
1 green pepper, chopped very finely
700ml (1¼ pints) tomato juice
salt and freshly ground pepper
croutons or garlic bread, to serve

Coarsely grate the cucumber into a large bowl, or dice for a more chunky soup. Blend the onion, garlic and tomatoes in a liquidizer or food processor (or grate the onion and garlic and finely chop the tomatoes). Add the oil, vinegar, lemon juice, tomato purée and pesto. Add this mixture to the cucumber with the green pepper. Add the tomato juice and season. Cover and chill thoroughly for about 6 hours. Serve with garlic bread or croutons and freshly ground pepper.

This chunky vegetable soup, traditionally eaten all over Spain, blends the pungency of raw onions and garlic with the tang of tomatoes and lemon delightfully. The ingredients may vary slightly from one region to another but it is always served ice-cold. Garlic and olive oil taken on a regular basis have been shown to significantly lower blood pressure. The basil in pesto has a wonderfully relaxing effect, which helps to reduce stress levels, while the antioxidant vitamins abundant in peppers, tomatoes and cucumber help to protect the heart and arteries from disease.

hawthorn & limeflower tea

Stress may play a part in your problem, so it is always a good idea to replace caffeinated drinks, which exacerbate tension, with relaxing herbal teas such as chamomile, lemon balm or limeflower.

SERVES I

Preparation time: 15 minutes

1 teaspoon hawthorn (flowers and leaves)
1 teaspoon limeflowers
250ml (8fl oz) boiling water

Place the herbs in a pot and pour over boiling water. Cover and leave to infuse for 10 minutes. Drink a cupful 3 times daily.

This light, sweet and astringent-tasting tisane combines two of the best herbal remedies for reducing blood pressure. The honey-flavoured limeflowers reduce tension levels in the body and relax the arteries, while hawthorn leaves and flowers regulate the diameter of the arteries and soften deposits inside the artery walls. Hawthorn also helps to reduce stress and anxiety and can be used as a balancer for both high and low blood pressure.

middle eastern stomach settler

THE SCIENCE BIT

It is important that you drink plenty of liquid to prevent dehydration when vomiting. Consult your doctor if persistent vomiting is accompanied by faintness, severe pain or fever.

SERVES 1

Preparation time: 10 minutes

3 small cinnamon sticks or one
  15cm (6in) stick of cinnamon bark
1 teaspoon ground cardamom
250ml (8fl oz) hot water

Grind the spices together in a coffee grinder. Place 1 teaspoon in a cup of hot water and sip slowly to bring relief.

This aromatic combination is popular in the Middle East for relieving nausea and apparently has been ever since the days of King Solomon, when the king's herbalist would grind the spices with a pestle and mortar to make this brew. Spices such as cinnamon and cardamom encourage the downward movement of energy in the digestive tract and so help to settle the stomach. Their highly antiseptic volatile oils are excellent for combating infection.

NAUSEA

ginger beer

THE SCIENCE BIT

Whatever the cause, one of the best and most delicious remedies for nausea is ginger. In a study in 1996, ginger effectively relieved motion sickness in 75 per cent of cases.

SERVES 1

Preparation time: 5 minutes plus
1 week fermenting time

For the starter:
15g (½oz) dried brewer's yeast
450ml (¾ pint) warm water
2 teaspoons ground ginger
2 teaspoons sugar

To feed the 'plant':
6 teaspoons ground ginger
6 teaspoons sugar

To make up:
750g (1¾lb) sugar
1.2 litres (2 pints) warm water
juice of 2 lemons
3 litres (5 pints) cold water

Place the starter ingredients in a glass jar with a lid. Stir well, cover and put in a warm place, such as a sunny windowsill. Leave for 24 hours then 'feed' daily for 6 days with 1 teaspoon ground ginger and 1 teaspoon sugar.

After 7 days strain the 'plant' through a sieve. Dissolve the sugar in the warm water in a large bowl or jug. Add the lemon juice, cold water and the liquid from the 'plant' and mix well. Bottle, in corked bottles, for at least seven days to mature. Serve with a sprig of fresh mint or lemon balm. Stored in a cool place, ginger beer will keep for about a week.

Tasty and invigorating, ginger beer makes a refreshing, non-alcoholic, sparkling drink, warming in the winter, thirst-quenching in the summer. Cultivating the 'plant' at home takes commitment as it needs 'feeding' every day but it is well worth the effort. Whatever the cause of nausea and vomiting, ginger is the best remedy, and it is perfectly safe to take throughout pregnancy. Sip ginger beer at intervals throughout the day whenever you feel queasy.

DRINKS FOR HEALING THE SOUL AND THE SPIRIT

introduction

While you might be surprised at the extent to which the common foodstuffs from our kitchens can benefit the health of our bodies, you may be even more amazed to know that they also have the power to influence the state of our minds and our emotions. Take depression, for example. Within our brains there are chemicals which help to transmit messages from one nerve cell to another. Two such chemicals that have a significant effect upon our mood, known as serotonin and noradrenaline, are made from the things we eat and drink. If our levels of these substances are low, we may have a tendency to feel low-spirited or depressed, and this can be reversed by eating specific foods.

Sweet and high-carbohydrate foods are mood-elevating. Dried fruits, such as apricots, bananas, figs and dates, and whole grains like wheat, barley and oats can be made into drinks that can give you natural highs! Serotonin and noradrenaline are also made from amino acids found in certain protein foods, including fish and poultry, nuts and seeds.

Foods can also work in a more general way by supplying nutrition to support the work of the nervous system. Fruits and vegetables that are rich in vitamin C will help to protect us against the effects of stress. B vitamins are vital for our nerves and by including whole grains, nuts and seeds, green vegetables – broccoli, spinach, cabbage and asparagus – and milk in

our drinks we will be helping to keep our mood stable. Green vegetables, nuts and seeds, oats, milk products and dried fruits are rich in minerals that are essential for the nervous system, particularly calcium and magnesium.

Some foods we choose because they harmonize our soul and spirit with the changing cycle of the seasons – hence we drink winter warmers and summer coolers, autumn boosters and Spring renewals. Others are particularly comforting when we feel in need of a little tender loving care. Often the foods we choose to make us feel better have childhood connections with love and nurture. Perhaps this is the reason why we sometimes reach for sweet foods to comfort us; sweets are traditionally given to children as treats and rewards and, of course, breast milk, too, is sweet. According to Ayurveda, sweet foods increase kapha and induce a feeling of inner security and calm.

The addition of herbs and spices to our drinks to support us emotionally is the icing on the cake. Several of these such as lemon balm, St John's Wort and rosemary have the ability to lift the spirits and restore our joie de vivre. Others like lavender, chamomile, catmint, limeflower and vervain can calm our anxiety and allow restful sleep. Warming spices like cinnamon, ginger and cardamom are not only delicious in winter warming drinks but increase our energy and our ability to confront problems in our lives. Some herbs, including ginseng and licorice, can almost miraculously enhance our resilience to the stresses we encounter and help us to maintain our equilibrium almost against all odds. So while the drinks to follow will, hopefully, delight your taste buds, perhaps they will also reach your inner parts to give you nourishment and support in your daily life.

provence lavender & lemon balm tisane

THE SCIENCE BIT
Some time for reflection may allow you to see the underlying causes of your anxiety and suggest what changes you can make in your life to ease the situation.

SERVES 2–3
Preparation time: 20 minutes

2 teaspoons lavender flowers
2 teaspoons lemon balm leaves
600ml (1 pint) boiling water
honey to taste (optional)

Place the herbs in a teapot and pour over boiling water. Cover and leave to infuse for 10-15 minutes. Drink a cupful 3 times daily, or more if required. Sweeten with honey if liked.

The lavender from Provence in France is famous for its magnificent aroma and flavour. Combined with lemon balm in this recipe it makes an exquisitely refreshing tea that tastes good enough for even the faint-hearted to enjoy. Lavender has a wonderfully relaxing effect on both mind and body and is excellent for reducing anxiety and some stress-related symptoms such as headaches, insomnia and palpitations. Similarly, lemon balm has a naturally sedative effect, enhancing relaxation and inducing sleep.

italian potato, tomato & basil soup

SERVES 6

Preparation time: 1 hour 10 minutes

4 tablespoons olive oil
1 large onion, peeled and sliced
1 bay leaf
1kg (2¼lb) potatoes, peeled and chopped roughly
salt and freshly ground pepper
1.5 litres (2½ pints) water
450g (1lb) tomatoes, skinned and chopped
2 handfuls of fresh basil leaves

Heat 1 tablespoon of oil in a large pan. Add the onion and bay leaf and cook over medium heat for 4–5 minutes. Add the potatoes and a little salt, cover and cook over low heat for 5 minutes. Add the water, bring to the boil and simmer, covered, for about 20 minutes, until the potatoes are soft. Without draining, mash loosely with a potato masher; do not blend. Warm 1 tablespoon of oil in a pan. Add the tomatoes and cook over a medium heat until the mixture starts to thicken. Break up the tomatoes to form a sauce-like consistency. Season to taste and stir into the potato mixture. Combine the basil with 2 tablespoons of oil in a blender and season with salt and pepper. Serve with a spoonful of basil purée swirled into each bowl and plenty of freshly ground black pepper.

My favourite of all soup recipes, this blend of potato, tomato and basil tastes like the epitomy of perfection. The nutritious potato provides valuable nutrients to support the nervous system such as B vitamins, vitamin C and potassium; the tomatoes provide vitamins A and E and plenty of iron.

banana calmer

THE SCIENCE BIT

When stress or anxiety weigh heavily upon us and interfere with our ability to relax and reflect, we can look to the world of plants to help restore some balance and harmony.

SERVES I

Preparation time: 5 minutes

250ml (8fl oz) milk
I banana, peeled and sliced
4 ice cubes
I tablespoon honey
pinch of ground or freshly grated
    nutmeg, plus extra to serve

Blend all the ingredients in a liquidizer or food processor until smooth. Serve sprinkled with extra nutmeg, if liked.

This smooth, creamy and comforting banana milk shake will help to soothe your mind. The high starch content and nutritional qualities of bananas may be wonderfully grounding when you are burning up lots of nervous energy. With its mild soothing effect, this sweet drink is excellent for calming your restlessness, especially if it's caused by overwork and stress.

greek lettuce soup

THE SCIENCE BIT

If you are having trouble mentally switching off, try drinking calming herbal teas such as chamomile, limeflower, mint, lemon balm or catmint. They are ideal for relieving tense muscles and slowing down an overactive mind.

SERVES 4

Preparation time: 20 minutes plus
  3–4 hours chilling time

1 tablespoon olive oil
2 medium onions, peeled and sliced
2 potatoes, peeled and diced
1 garlic clove, crushed
1 large lettuce, chopped
900ml (1½ pints) chicken or
  vegetable stock
salt and freshly ground pepper
3 tablespoons thick natural yogurt
freshly chopped mint leaves,
  to garnish

Heat the oil in a saucepan and gently fry the onions, potatoes and garlic for 5 minutes. Add the lettuce, stock and seasoning. Bring to the boil, cover and simmer over low heat until the vegetables are tender. Leave the soup to cool for a short time. Blend in a liquidizer then stir in the yogurt. Chill in the refrigerator for 3-4 hours. Serve garnished with mint.

This delicious, cold soup is ideal for calming you down on hot flustery days. The cooling effects of the yogurt and lettuce can help you slow down on days when your mind will not rest. The mint garnish helps to stimulate blood flow to the head, clearing the mind.

serenity
smoothie

THE SCIENCE BIT

Oats, wheat, barley and rice have a calming effect on the body and mind, as do almonds and dates. Eaten with mild spices, these ingredients can help induce a peaceful, meditative state.

SERVES 1

Preparation time: 10 minutes

1 tablespoon ground almonds
100g (4oz) dates (stones removed)
350ml (12fl oz) water or rice milk
1 teaspoon ground ginger

Blend all the ingredients together in a liquidizer or food processor until smooth.

A deliciously sweet drink that will nourish and settle your mind. The sweetness of the rice milk, almonds and dates is offset by the spicy flavour of the ginger that brings in more than a hint of the East. All the ingredients have a strengthening and stabilizing effect on the nerves, helping to improve memory and concentration – no wonder these foods have been popular for bringing peace of mind in India for thousands of years.

middle eastern avocado soup

THE SCIENCE BIT

Always eat a good diet regularly and sleep well. Vitamins B and C and minerals zinc, potassium, calcium, magnesium and iron are considered the most important nutrients in the battle against stress.

SERVES 4

Preparation time: 20 minutes plus 1 hour chilling time

3 large avocados, peeled and chopped
500ml (16fl oz) vegetable or chicken stock
juice of 1½ lemons
6 spring onions, chopped
3 garlic cloves, peeled
250ml (8fl oz) crème fraîche or natural yogurt
1–2.5cm (½–1in) piece fresh root ginger, peeled and grated
salt and freshly ground pepper
fresh parsley and avocado slices, to garnish (optional)

Place the avocado in a blender with the stock and lemon juice and blend until smooth. Add the spring onions, garlic, crème fraîche (or yogurt) and ginger to taste, then blend again. Season with salt and pepper. Cover and chill for 1 hour. Add more stock, if too thick, and lemon juice to taste. Serve garnished with parsley and avocado slices, if liked.

In countries like Turkey and Israel they are very fond of chilled avocado soup which is often served as a main dish in the summer. It is thick and creamy and in this recipe the blandness of the avocado is offset by the pungency of the ginger. Avocados are rich in nutrients for the nervous system, including vitamins B and C, potassium and iron. They calm and strengthen the nerves and are excellent during times of stress.

STRESS RELIEF

tanzanian banana & coconut milk

SERVES 1–2
Preparation time: 10 minutes

3 medium-sized, ripe bananas
250ml (8fl oz) coconut milk
ground cinnamon, to serve
  (optional)

Place the bananas and coconut milk in a liquidizer and blend until smooth. Sprinkle cinnamon on the top when serving, if liked.

Many recipes in Tanzania, including soups, stews and desserts, are based on bananas and plantain and often combined with coconut. The mixture of the two sweet tastes in this recipe is wonderful. Both bananas and coconut are highly nutritious, rich in B vitamins, calcium, magnesium, iron and potassium. They are strengthening, even rejuvenating and with their grounding and calming effect are ideal foods for relieving stress.

nettle & cabbage soup

THE SCIENCE BIT

Certain foods and herbs such as watercress, dandelion leaves, young nettle tops, cabbage and leeks have the remarkable ability to detoxify the system.

SERVES 4

Preparation time: 45 minutes

1 tablespoon olive oil
1 large onion, peeled and chopped
2 leeks, washed and sliced
100g (4oz) cabbage, chopped
1.2 litres (2 pints) vegetable or
  chicken stock
salt and freshly ground pepper
2 handfuls nettle tops, washed
2 tablespoons chopped fresh
  parsley or coriander
ground nutmeg and boiled egg slices
  to garnish, (optional)

Heat the oil in a saucepan, add the onion and cook until soft. Add the leeks and cabbage, cover and cook on a low heat for 10 minutes. Add the stock and seasoning. Bring to the boil and simmer for 20 minutes, adding the nettles for the last few minutes. Remove from the heat and blend. Add the parsley or coriander before serving and garnish with nutmeg and slices of boiled egg, if liked.

The abundant chlorophyll in nettles gives this soup a wonderfully vibrant colour that makes you feel healthy just looking at it. Bursting with vitamins, minerals and trace elements, it nourishes and cleanses at the same time. An antiseptic, a diuretic, a tonic to the liver and a laxative, cabbage makes an ideal Spring tonic, explaining its ancient reputation for purifying the blood. Similarly, nettles stimulate the liver and kidneys, cleansing the body of toxins and wastes, and restore vitality to the system.

tuscan spring tonic

SERVES 1

Preparation time: 5 minutes

250ml (8fl oz) carrot juice
125ml (4fl oz) celery juice
1 garlic clove
1 handful of fresh parsley
sprigs of parsley, to garnish

Blend all the ingredients together in a liquidizer or food processor. Serve with a garnish of parsley.

Ever since the 17th century celery has been popular with the Italians. In fact, the old French name for celery is *sceleri d'Italie*. Wonderfully aromatic, celery blends well with the rather similar taste of parsley, the pungency of garlic and the sweetness of carrot, to make this thick, highly nutritious vegetable juice. Perfect as a Spring cleanser, celery, parsley and carrots all have diuretic properties, aiding the elimination of toxins via the kidneys, while garlic invigorates the whole body, disinfecting and cleansing as it goes.

welsh dandelion beer

THE SCIENCE BIT

Drinks for Spring need to be able to renew our energy and vitality and at the same time detoxify the body of toxins accumulated from the sedentary habits of the winter months.

SERVES 6–8

Preparation time: 50 minutes plus
 3 days fermenting time and
 1 week storage time

225g (8oz) young dandelion plants
4.5 litres (8 pints) water
15g (½oz) root ginger, sliced and
 bruised
finely peeled rind and juice of
 1 lemon
450g (1lb) demerara sugar
25g (1oz) cream of tartar
7g (¼oz) dried brewer's yeast

Dig up complete young dandelion plants, wash them well and remove all the fibrous roots, leaving the main tap root. Place in a large saucepan with the water, ginger and lemon rind. Bring to the boil and simmer for 10 minutes. Strain and pour on to the sugar and cream of tartar in a fermentation bucket. Stir until the sugar has dissolved. Start the yeast following the instructions and add it to the lukewarm must with the lemon juice. Cover and leave in a warm room for 3 days. Strain into screw-top bottles. It will be ready to drink after 1 week and, if stored in a cool place, will keep for about a month.

This traditional Welsh recipe makes a beer that is excellent for quenching thirst and not very alcoholic. The combination of the bitterness of dandelions and the pungency of ginger is perfect for our purposes in Spring. The bitter taste stimulates the function of the liver, the great detoxifying organ of the body, while the ginger's pungency has the effect of revitalizing the whole system, improving digestion and absorption while ensuring the removal of toxins and wastes.

carob inspiration

SERVES 2–3

Preparation time: 50 minutes

600ml (1 pint) milk or soya milk
4 teaspoons carob powder
5 cardamom pods, crushed
honey to taste

Add 1 tablespoonful of milk to the carob powder and stir into a smooth paste. Heat the rest of the milk in a pan, add the cardamom pods, then cover and keep almost at simmering point for 20–30 minutes. Strain the milk, return to the pan and add the carob paste. Stir and heat gently for a further 2 minutes. Remove from the heat.

The carob bean is delicious in warm drinks, bringing a hint of Mediterranean sunshine to a gloomy day. It is naturally sweet and energy-giving, a wonderfully comforting and grounding drink. Cardamom and milk are an excellent combination as cardamoms have the ability to dispel the mucus-forming properties of milk. When making this recipe, it is important not to boil the cardamoms.

avocado dream

THE SCIENCE BIT

Foods, herbs and spices can all play their part in nurturing the nervous system and many of them have specifically mood-elevating properties that help to dispel negativity and lift the spirits.

SERVES 1
Preparation time: 10 minutes

1 ripe avocado, peeled and sliced
1 garlic clove, peeled
juice of ½ lemon
300ml (½ pint) rice milk
salt and freshly ground pepper
sprigs of fresh coriander, to garnish

Place the avocado in a blender with the garlic, lemon juice and rice milk. Blend until smooth. Season with salt and pepper and serve garnished with fresh coriander.

The smooth creamy taste and texture of the avocado and rice milk are bought to life by the bite and tang of the garlic, lemon juice and coriander to produce a drink that tastes good and does you good! Avocados are ideal for those who suffer from feelings of depression as they are rich in vitamins B and E for the hormonal system and, at the same time, they calm and strengthen the nervous system. They contain the amino acid tryptphan which helps to create serotonin, the brain chemical that promotes relaxation and is responsible for maintaining mood balance. A deficit of serotonin leads to depression.

DEPRESSION

mood-lifting tea

THE SCIENCE BIT

Black pepper, with its pungent taste and warming properties, is excellent for warding off lethargy. Its stimulating properties help to dispel nervous debility, low spirits and depression.

SERVES 2–3

Preparation time: 10 minutes plus
1 hour to simmer

600ml (1 pint) cold water
4 black peppercorns
4 cardamom pods
1 cinnamon stick
4 cloves
few slices of fresh root ginger
milk and/or honey to taste

Place the water and spices in a pan and heat to nearly boiling (never boil). Cover and simmer for an hour. Strain and serve. Add a little milk and/or honey if you like. Drink a cupful 2–3 times daily.

Cardamom is not only a delicious spice but also an energy tonic and restorative to warm and inspire. Cardamom comes from India, where it has long been used in Ayurvedic medicine to lift the spirits, dispel cold and depression, restore strength and vitality, and to induce a calm, meditative state of mind.

DEPRESSION

lemon balm tea

THE SCIENCE BIT

Certain foodstuffs can lift the spirits by raising endorphin levels. Dried fruits, such as dates, figs and apricots, and carbohydrates like rice, as well as honey, all increase these mood-enhancing endorphins.

SERVES 2–3

Preparation time: 20 minutes

25g (1oz) fresh lemon balm leaves
600ml (1 pint) boiling water

Place the lemon balm in a teapot and pour over boiling water. Put the lid on and leave to infuse for 10-15 minutes. Drink, hot or cold, up to four times a day.

A wonderful remedy for the nerves, lemon balm restores energy and lifts low spirits as well as calming tension and anxiety.

Many of us feel tired, low, or lacking in enthusiasm, inspiration, or even interest from time to time. This often occurs in winter and particularly affects people who tend to feel cold and lethargic in cold weather. Foods with a cold quality, such as dairy products, sugar and wheat products, are best reduced to a minimum in these instances, while warming spices – ginger, cardamom, cloves and cinnamon – are just the thing to lift the spirits. By increasing the circulation and thereby the efficiency of every cell in the body, these spices increase energy and impart a sense of wellbeing.

szechwan soup

THE SCIENCE BIT

Fruit, vegetables, herbs and spices provide many warming remedies that stimulate the circulation and dilate the blood vessels so that warmth reaches even those cold extremities.

SERVES 4

Preparation time: 1 hour 10 minutes

5 dried Chinese mushrooms (or any mushroom of your choice)

25g (1oz) rice noodles

1.5 litres (2½ pints) chicken stock

100g (4oz) chopped cooked chicken

225g (8oz) bamboo shoots, tinned, drained

2 teaspoons freshly grated root ginger

2 garlic cloves, finely chopped

1 egg, beaten

½ tablespoon tomato purée

1 tablespoon soy sauce

1 tablespoon cider vinegar

2 teaspoons sesame oil

3 spring onions, finely chopped

salt and freshly ground pepper

Soak the Chinese mushrooms in hot water in a bowl for 30 minutes, then drain and chop. Soak the noodles in cold water for 20 minutes, drain and cut into short lengths. Heat the chicken stock in a large pan and bring to the boil. Add the mushrooms, chicken, bamboo shoots, ginger, garlic and noodles. Reduce the heat, cover and simmer gently for 4 minutes, then add the egg in a fine stream, stirring all the time. Remove the pan from the heat and add the remaining ingredients, reserving a few spring onions to garnish. Season with salt and pepper and serve topped with spring onionss.

The combination of the onions, garlic and ginger of this centuries-old hot and sour Chinese soup has a powerfully stimulating effect, increasing blood flow throughout the body and dispelling winter cold most effectively.

zanzibar zinger

THE SCIENCE BIT

Poor circulation may make you feel the cold more than others, especially in your extremities. You be prone to problems such as chilblains, low energy, sluggish digestion and constipation, particularly in winter.

SERVES 1

Preparation time: 15 minutes

300ml (½ pint) grapefruit juice
3 cloves
1 cinnamon stick
1 tablespoon honey
nutmeg to taste

Place the grapefruit juice, cloves and cinnamon in a pan and heat. Keep the mixture almost at simmering point for 5 minutes. Remove from the heat and strain. Stir in the honey and sprinkle with a dash of nutmeg.

This exotic blend of tangy grapefruit and a medley of spices makes a wonderfully warming drink for a cold winter's day. Grapefruit is rich in vitamin C and bioflavonoids which dilate and strengthen the blood vessels and improve the circulation through them. Cloves, from the beautiful shores of Zanzibar (once the most important trade centre in East Africa), as well as cinnamon and nutmeg dilate the blood vessels and stimulate the heart and circulation.

medieval ginger cordial

SERVES 2–3

Preparation time: 20 minutes

100g (4oz) dried figs
¼ teaspoon ground allspice
a few slices of fresh root ginger
¼ teaspoon ground nutmeg
1 cinnamon stick
4 cloves
600ml (1 pint) ginger beer
1 teaspoon lemon juice

Stew the figs in enough water to cover them, until soft, then blend to a smooth paste. Return to the pan, add the spices and ginger beer, and heat slowly, then simmer, covered, for 10 minutes. Add the lemon juice. Strain and drink a cupful hot when required.

Truly invigorating and spicy, this cordial has been a traditional favourite in monasteries since the Dark Ages. It stimulates the heart and circulation, making you feel warm right down to your toes.

caribbean lime & cayenne syrup

THE SCIENCE BIT

You only have to experience the burning sensation on the tongue and then that warm feeling in the stomach, to know that ginger, garlic, onions, leeks and cayenne are just the thing for a cold winter's day.

SERVES 2

Preparation time: 20 minutes

600ml (1 pint) water
1.3kg (3lb) sugar
1 egg white
600ml (1 pint) lime juice
1–2 teaspoons cayenne pepper,
  to taste

Whisk the water, sugar and egg white together in a saucepan. Bring to the boil and simmer slowly for 10 minutes. Add the lime juice and simmer for a further minute. Add the cayenne, stir and leave to cool. Bottle and seal well. Take two tablespoons in a cup of hot water when required.

Cayenne is a major stimulant to the heart and circulation, perfect for warming chilly people and for warding off 'blues' and lethargy.

french onion soup

SERVES 4

Preparation time: 1 hour 10 minutes

1 tablespoon olive oil
6 onions, peeled and sliced into thin rings
4 garlic cloves, thinly slivered
1 teaspoon sugar
1 tablespoon plain flour
1.2 litres (2 pints) vegetable or chicken stock
1 tablespoon fresh thyme
1 tablespoon fresh rosemary
salt and freshly ground pepper
1 French baguette
175g (6oz) Gruyère cheese, grated

Heat the oil in a large pan over a low heat. Add the onions and cook for about 30 minutes. Add the garlic and cook for another minute or so. Then stir in the sugar and flour and cook for 1–2 minutes until the onions turn golden. Stir in the stock, bring to the boil and simmer, covered, for 45 minutes. Add the thyme, rosemary and seasoning.

While the soup is cooking, cut the French bread into 2.5cm (1in) slices and bake in an oven preheated to 180°C (350°F, gas mark 4) for about 20 minutes, turning once, until lightly golden. Place 4 ovenproof crocks on a baking sheet and ladle in the soup to 1cm (½in) from the rim. Float a piece of bread on the top of each bowl and cover well with grated cheese. Place under a hot grill until the cheese is golden brown and bubbling. Serve immediately.

With their pungent warming properties, onions have the ability to stimulate the circulation, dilate the arteries, lower blood pressure, reduce harmful cholesterol levels and help guard against heart attacks.

indian rose syrup & coconut milk

THE SCIENCE BIT

For our emotions themselves the almost miraculous world of flowers offers a wealth of healing, for flowers seem to have the power to heal us on all levels of our being.

SERVES I

Preparation time: 15 minutes plus
   steep overnight

1 tablespoon rose syrup
250ml (8fl oz) coconut milk
ice cubes

To make rose syrup collect rose petals, weigh them and place in a bowl with an equal weight of sugar. Mash the petals and sugar together, cover and leave overnight. Strain through a fine sieve, pour into clean bottles and store in the refrigerator. Stir a tablespoonful of syrup into a cup of coconut milk. Add ice and dilute with a little water, if required. The syrup will keep for about a month.

Just tasting this sweet nectar is enough to bring joy to the heart. Roses have long been associated with love and all affairs of the heart. They have a wonderfully uplifting and restorative effect and can be thought of whenever you feel tense, anxious, depressed, angry, lonely and upset. They are specifically for those who lack love in their lives. In India coconut is seen as a gift from the gods to human beings and a token of good luck in romantic relationships.

heartsease & chamomile infusion

THE SCIENCE BIT

We can use foods and herbs to help support and heal us as we work through our emotional problems, so that the stress they impose does not lead to nervous exhaustion and physical illness.

SERVES 1

Preparation time: 20 minutes

½ teaspoon heartease flowers
½ teaspoon chamomile flowers
250ml (8fl oz) boiling water
honey to taste (optional)

Place the herbs in a small teapot and pour over boiling water. Cover and leave to infuse for 10–15 minutes before serving. Sweeten with honey if you like.

Wild pansy or heartease derives its name from its ability to heal the heart, to soothe the pain of separation from loved ones and to ease a broken heart. Chamomile also helps to ease emotional pain, to soothe anger and conflict and to release tension accumulating from inner problems that might otherwise contribute to stress-related illness and insomnia. The combination of the two makes a pleasant light tisane, perfect for promoting inner harmony.

borage & lemon balm fruit cup

THE SCIENCE BIT

Flowers can act as catalysts to self awareness and understanding, to releasing emotional blocks and allowing us to let go of pain that results from broken relationships, grief and trauma.

SERVES 2–3
Preparation time: 15 minutes

600ml (1 pint) apple or pear juice
1 handful fresh borage flowers
1 handful fresh lemon balm leaves

Heat the fruit juice in a pan until almost boiling. Place 1 teaspoon of each of the herbs in a jug and pour over the hot fruit juice. Cover and leave to cool. Strain into a clean jug and float a few borage flowers and lemon balm leaves to decorate. Serve with ice if desired.

Borage flowers and lemon balm leaves floated in fruit juices, such as apple or pear, make delightfully refreshing drinks for a hot summer's day that can, at the same time, help to ease emotional pain. Borage has a generally relaxing effect and is famous for its ability to dispel grief and sadness and to aid the heavy-hearted, broken-hearted or down-hearted. Lemon balm lifts the spirits, balances the emotions and imparts inner strength and courage.

mintade

The idea of bliss on a hot summer's day is to relax in the shade of a lovely old fruit tree and idly while away the hours lazily sipping a cooling fruity drink from time to time.

SERVES 2–3

Preparation time: 15 minutes plus
2 hours to steep

1½ lemons, washed
2 tablespoons fresh mint leaves,
  crushed
1½ tablespoons sugar
600ml (1 pint) boiling water
ice cubes
sprigs of mint and fresh lemon slices,
  to garnish

Slice the lemons, saving the juice. Place in a jug with the mint and sugar. Pour on boiling water and leave to steep for 2 hours. Strain and serve in glasses over ice, garnished with sprigs of mint and lemon slices.

No other herb can rival the refreshing taste of fresh mint leaves in summer and when combined with lemon and ice they make an ideal drink for when you are hot and thirsty. Interestingly, in the language of flowers, mint represents eternal refreshment. The cooling effect of mint is experienced on the tongue the minute it is tasted, and this soon disperses throughout the rest of the body. Its ability to revive mind and body is particularly welcome after a heavy lunch when lethargy on a hot afternoon threatens to overcome our efficiency at work.

cold cucumber & mint soup

THE SCIENCE BIT

There are certain foods and herbs that make perfect summer drinks including cucumber, watercress, bananas, melon, mangoes, elderflowers, mint, lemon balm and yogurt.

SERVES 3–4

Preparation time: 15 minutes plus
1 hour refrigeration time

1 large cucumber, peeled and diced
6 spring onions, trimmed and
chopped
250ml (8fl oz) water (or vegetable
or chicken stock)
3 tablespoons Greek natural yogurt
juice of 1 lemon
6 sprigs fresh mint
salt and freshly ground pepper
cucumber slices and fresh herbs,
to garnish

Blend the cucumber, spring onions and water (or stock) together until smooth. Add the yogurt and lemon juice. Strip the mint leaves from the stems, reserving a few to garnish, if liked, then finely chop and stir into the yogurt mixture. Season to taste. Cover and refrigerate for 1 hour. Garnish with cucumber slices and fresh herbs before serving.

The cooling, thirst-quenching cucumber is a perfect partner for mint, the most refreshing of herbs. Together they make an exquisite tasting cold soup for a hot day, the mild pungency of the mint and spring onions contrasting with the blandness of the cucumber. The yogurt gives it a lovely creamy consistency and additional cooling properties.

english elderflower cordial

THE SCIENCE BIT

Not only do elderflowers taste delightful in cold drinks, but they also have cooling properties themselves.

SERVES 4

Preparation time: 20 minutes

1.2 litres (2 pints) water
1.3 kg (3lb) sugar
1 lemon, sliced
25 large elderflower heads
75g (3oz) citric acid
sparkling or still mineral water
   to dilute

Place the water in a large pan and bring to the boil. Add the sugar and lemon and remove from the heat until the sugar dissolves. Place on the heat again and bring to the boil. Add the elderflower heads and citric acid. Bring to the boil once more, remove from the heat and allow to stand until cool. Strain and bottle in clean bottles with corks. This can be drunk immediately. Stored in a cool place it should keep approximately 3 months. When serving, dilute with 5 parts water and add ice.

This delicately scented cordial makes a light, fruity tasting and wonderfully refreshing drink. One sip and immediately you are transported to the perfection of a warm summer's afternoon in the beauty of England's countryside. The cooling effect of elderflowers is brought about in two main ways. By bringing blood to the surface of the body, heat is released through the pores of the skin, and by their diuretic action, excess heat as well as toxins are eliminated via the kidneys.

italian tomato juice

SERVES 3–4

Preparation time: 10 minutes

450g (1lb) ripe tomatoes, chopped
2 teaspoons lemon juice
3 teaspoons Worcestershire sauce
1 teaspoon soy sauce
salt to taste
pinch of cayenne pepper
fresh or dried thyme, to garnish

Blend together the tomatoes, lemon juice, Worcestershire sauce, soy sauce, salt and cayenne pepper in a liquidizer or food processor. Strain and serve over ice and with a garnish of thyme.

The bright red 'love apple' as the tomato used to be called, always looks inviting in drinks and this thick, piquant juice is no exception. Tomatoes have been popular in Italian cuisine ever since the Middle Ages when a Fra Serenio brought the precious seeds back from his travels in China. Rich in antioxidant vitamins and minerals, they boost energy and vitality, aid the elimination of toxins and enhance the body's fight against infection.

french apple & cinnamon tea

THE SCIENCE BIT

Drinks packed with vitamins and minerals made from apples, pears, plums, blackberries and elderberries, provide vital nutrients for the immune system and serve to prepare us for the onslaught of winter.

SERVES 2–3

Preparation time: 15 minutes

4 apples, washed and sliced
600ml (1 pint) water
2 tablespoons honey
1 teaspoon ground cinnamon

Place the apples in a pan, add the water, cover and cook on a low heat until soft. Strain then stir in the honey and cinnamon. Serve hot.

The traditional combination of apple and cinnamon works well in this sweet and spicy tea. The tart flavour and cold properties of the apples are balanced by the sweetness and warming properties of the honey and cinnamon. Jean Valnet, the French phytotherapist, recommends apple tea to be taken daily to prevent cold and flu viruses and to ward off arthritis and gout.

elderberry rob

THE SCIENCE BIT

Spices added to enhance the flavour of the fruit have the extra benefit of stimulating the circulation, keeping us warm as the weather turns colder.

SERVES 2

Preparation time: 25 minutes

450g (1lb) fresh elderberries
450g (1lb) brown sugar

Strip the berries from their stems, wash and then crush them. Place in a pan with the sugar. Bring slowly to the boil and simmer until a syrupy consistency is reached. Pass through a sieve and bottle in clean, airtight bottles. Take 1–2 tablespoons in a cup of hot water regularly as a preventative or at the onset of cold symptoms. This recipe works well with other fruit such as blackberries and blackcurrants.

This rich dark-red cordial is a storehouse of vitamins A and C, and a delicious syrupy remedy for preventing and treating coughs, colds and flu, sore throats and fevers. Until the end of the 19th century hot elderberry drinks were sold on the streets of London on cold winter days and nights to give cheer to workers and travellers and to keep out the cold. Cinnamon was often added to elderberry rob to enhance its warming effect.

appendix

EQUIPMENT

All the drinks in this book are very quick and easy to make providing you have a few basic pieces of equipment. The most basic equipment of all is, of course, your two hands and some bowls or jugs, and they will very often prove quite adequate. However, a simple piece of machinery very often will do in a few seconds what it would take your hands a lot longer to accomplish.

Blenders, liquidizers and food processors

These machines can be used interchangeably and are designed to blend all parts of a variety of ingredients together until even-textured and smooth. In smooth soups, for example, the ingredients are cooked as instructed in the recipe then, before serving, are blended by high-speed shredding. The process transforms the mixture of chunky vegetables in liquid into a homogenous consistency.

Fruit drinks and smoothies prepared in a blender, liquidizer or food processor have the advantage of retaining all their fibre, which is well known to be vital to the health of the bowel, as well as having the effect of reducing cholesterol levels.

If you do not possess a blender it is possible to blend to some degree by hand but it is a much lengthier process. When making a smoothie for example, you can mash the ripe fruit with a fork then blend it with the other ingredients in a bowl. The result will never be as smooth and creamy but it will be equally tasty and just as good for you. If you want to incorporate healthy drinks into your daily routine, however, it would be worth investing in a machine.

An electric hand blender is a good alternative if you are blending large quantities – when making soup, for example. If you use a liquidizer this can involve a lot of work, as you have to transfer the ingredients from the pan to the liquidizer to be blended in batches. It is often very much easier to insert a hand blender into the ingredients wherever they happen to be – in a bowl, a jug or a pan – and switch it on. Within a few minutes or even seconds the work is done.

Juicers

Juicers are designed to extract the juice from fruits, vegetables and herbs while leaving the fibre behind, and there is a variety of different types available. Many of us have been juicing for years using a simple lemon squeezer to extract our citrus juices, and this still remains a good option. Electric citrus juicers, which are based on the same principle, significantly reduce the amount of elbow power needed.

It is possible to extract juices from fruit and vegetables by hand but it is hard work. Grate the fruit or vegetable into a bowl, place it in a piece of clean muslin and squeeze as hard as you can. The amount of juice extracted will depend on your strength and persistence!

The juices of some vegetables, onion and cabbage, for example, can be extracted using a covering of honey or sugar which have hydroscopic properties that draw the liquid out.

To extract juices from other fruit and vegetables you really do need a juicer. There are several types of machine and the one you choose will depend on the kinds of ingredients you want to juice; how easy the machine is to take apart to wash and then reassemble; its size; and the price.

Centrifugal juicers, the least expensive, can cope with only small quantities of material at a time, but for most individual's purposes they serve quite adequately. Like the other types of machine they chop up the ingredients at high speed and then separate the juice from the pulp.

Masticating juicers are slightly more expensive but are more efficient as they cope better with hard bits of skin and pips.

Hydraulic juicers can cope with large quantities and extract more juice from the chopped-up pulp, but tend to cost the most. You get what you pay for.

Cleaning equipment

Wash all the equipment you use thoroughly after use to avoid contaminating and spoiling drinks with lingering tastes from former preparations. If strong-tasting ingredients do linger you may find that putting apple or lemon through the machine will not only resolve this but also help to remove stains on your equipment.

GENERAL ADVICE

Choosing ingredients

Whatever method you use to make your drinks, choose the best-quality ingredients you can; tired-looking fruits and vegetables will never match those freshly picked for either taste or goodness.

Use organic fruit and vegetables if available. As well as being free from the health risks associated with the use of pesticides, organic fruit and vegetables will often provide additional nutrients, since you do not usually need to peel them.

In order that nutrients (vitamins A and C and folic acid, in particular) that diminish during storage are not lost, it is a good idea to buy fresh ingredients in small quantities and use them quickly.

Bought juices It is always preferable to extract fruit and vegetable juices yourself, as freshly prepared drinks score highest in terms of maximum nutritional benefit. However, shop bought equivilants are well worth buying if you do not have the means to make your own. Look in health food shops for the more unusual juices, such as beetroot and cabbage.

Frozen, dried and tinned foods Fresh fruit and vegetables are best for all the recipes in this book, but if an ingredient is unavailable or out of season, frozen, dried or tinned versions will do. Choose tinned fruit preserved in fruit juice or water, rather than in a heavy syrup, and sun-dried fruits, such as apricots, rather than sulphur-dried versions, which can cause allergic reactions in some people.

Finishing touches

The garnishes used in the recipes – fruits, vegetables, herbs or spices – often enhance the medicinal benefits of the drinks. They also make your drinks look inviting, however, and add extra excitement to the taste.

The glasses or bowls in which you serve your drinks can add to their presentation so that you produce drinks that not only taste wonderful and do you a power of good but look tempting as well.

Drink as soon as possible

It is important to consume your drinks as soon as possible after preparation so that the maximum nutrition remains. Certain nutrients (folic acid and vitamins A and C, for instance), will diminish on exposure to light and air, standing and storing.

Soups can be kept for a day or two but freshly extracted vegetable and fruit juices and smoothies are best consumed immediately, since most of the goodness is lost within 20 minutes.

Juice fasting

Drinking only fruit and vegetable juices or water for a day (not more than once a week but recommended at least once a month) is excellent not only for cleansing the body thoroughly but also for invigorating body and mind. Juice fasting gives the whole digestive system a day off and is an excellent way to rid the body of toxins.

Grape juice is the most popular choice for juice fasts, whether drunk alone or with other juices. Look for recipes in the book that are detoxifying – ones that include grape, carrot, beetroot and apple, for example – or act as laxatives. Don't drink more than one glassful of pure carrot juice a day or more than four glassfuls a week.

Note: *Do not go on a juice fast if you are pregnant, if you suffer from anaemia or diabetes, or if you have an eating disorder. Consult your doctor if you are in doubt.*

Making herbal teas

To prepare herbal tea you need either a teapot or a small pan and a sieve. Use about 2 teaspoonfuls of dried herb (or 4 teaspoonfuls of fresh) to 600ml (1 pint) water. Vary the amount according to taste.

When using the soft parts of a herb, such as the flower, stems or leaves, place the herb in a warm teapot and pour over boiling water. Cover and leave to stand for 10 to 15 minutes to allow the hot water to extract the medicinal components from the plant. Use this method for basil, rosemary, thyme and lemon balm teas, for example.

When using the hard parts of a herb or spice – the seeds, bark or roots (cinnamon bark, coriander seed or ginger root, for example) – greater heat is required to extract the constituents. You will need to place them in a pan with cold water, bring to the boil, cover and simmer for 10 to 15 minutes. Strain and sweeten with honey if you like.

Quantities

1 teaspoon (level) = 5ml
1 tablespoon (level) = 15ml
1 cupful or glassful = 250ml (8fl oz)
1 small glassful = 90ml (3fl oz)
1 large glassful = 350ml (12fl oz)

useful terms

adaptogenic Helps to restore balance within the body

anaesthetic Deadens sensation and reduces pain

analgesic Pain relieving

antibacterial Destroys or stops the growth of bacterial infections

antibiotic Destroys or stops the growth of bacteria

antidiuretic Decreases urine production

antifungal Treats fungal infections

anti-inflammatory Reduces inflammation

antimicrobial Destroys or stops the growth of micro-organisms

antioxidant Prevents damage by free radicals and helps protects against degenerative disease

antiparasitical Kills parasites

antiseptic Prevents putrefaction

antispasmodic Prevents or relieves spasms or cramps

antiviral Destroys or stops the growth of viral infections

astringent Contracts tissue, drying and reducing secretions or discharges

bactericidal Able to destroy bacteria

decoction Herbal tea made from the hard parts of a plant, such as the seeds, bark or roots

decongestant Relieves congestion

detoxifying Eliminating toxins from the body

digestive Aids digestion

disinfectant Destroys or inhibits the activity of micro-organisms that cause disease

diuretic Promotes the flow of urine

endorphins Natural substances synthesized in the pineal gland which have an analgesic effect

expectorant Promotes expulsion of mucus from the repiratory tract

infusion Herbal tea made from the soft parts of a herb – the flower, stems or leaves

laxative Promotes evacuation of the bowels

panacea A remedy for all ills or disorders

relaxant Relaxes nerves and muscles

restorative Restores normal physiological activity and energy

stimulant Produces energy and increases circulation

tisane An infusion made from fresh or dried herbs

tonic Invigorates and tones the body and promotes wellbeing

index

PICTURE CREDITS